■ SCHOLASTIC

NO FUSS

C000062981

YEAR 5
PHOTOCOPIABLES

All you need to teach
11 curriculum subjects!

AGES

■ Levelled and linked to
the curriculum

■ Stand-alone photocopiable
activities

9-10

■ Ideal for mixed-age
classes

**Paul Noble and
Jean Noble**

AUTHORS
Paul Noble and Jean Noble

DEVELOPMENT EDITOR
Kate Pedlar

PROJECT EDITOR
Fabia Lewis

DESIGNERS
Q2a Media

COVER DESIGN
Anna Oliwa

ILLUSTRATOR
Jon Sayer

ACKNOWLEDGEMENTS
The Royal Mint for use of photographs of coins of the realm © Crown copyright.
Severn Trent Water Ltd for use of a water bill.

Text © 2008, Paul Noble and Jean Noble
© 2008, Scholastic Ltd

Published by Scholastic Ltd
Villiers House
Clarendon Avenue
Leamington Spa
Warwickshire
CV32 5PR
www.scholastic.co.uk

Designed using Adobe InDesign
Printed by Bell & Bain Ltd, Glasgow

1 2 3 4 5 6 7 8 9   8 9 0 1 2 3 4 5 6 7

British Library Cataloguing-in-Publication Data
A catalogue record for this book is available from the British Library.

ISBN 978-1407-10097-5

The rights of Paul Noble and Jean Noble to be identified as the authors of this work have been asserted by them in accordance with the Copyright, Designs and Patents Act 1988.

Crown copyright material reproduced under the terms of the Click Use Licence © Crown copyright.

Photocopiable pages first published in *Year Group Photocopiables Year 5* (first published 2003).

www.scholastic.co.uk

CONTENTS

CONTENTS

INTRODUCTION

This is a straightforward compilation of stand-alone photocopiable activities for children in Year 5. Instead of including lengthy teachers' notes, we have devised a concise and factual **curriculum grid**, which, in note form, cross-references the content of the sheets to the National Curriculum, the Primary Framework and where appropriate, to the Curriculum for Excellence (Scotland). Objectives for each activity sheet are stated and brief guidance notes are given to its use.

Within the curriculum grid, links are also made to National Curriculum Attainment Targets and attainment levels, as well as to the non-statutory Attainment Targets in RE and the non-statutory framework at Key Stage 2 for PSHE and Citizenship. Before you use any sheet it is recommended that you refer to the curriculum grid so that you are clear about the sheet's objectives and are aware of any special demands made by the activity.

The 'photocopiable worksheet' has not always had a good press – there are copying issues to contend with as well as the occasional question mark over quality. Yet arguably, in spite of the high-tech gizmos now available, they are still one of the most useful teaching aids invented since a stick of chalk first squeaked its way across a chalkboard. Nevertheless, when a worksheet is handed out, you cannot assume that intellectual activity is immediately stimulated: it still remains for a teacher to capture children's interest and to provide the intellectual stimulus and practical experience that may be required to make the worksheet work.

Year 5 is often regarded as a preparatory year, when the countdown to Year 6 (a year for national testing) really begins. It has sometimes been referred to as 'a year to panic', which is a pity, because Year 5 children can be a rewarding group to teach. They have sufficient learning, skills and maturity to take on increasingly challenging tasks and the quality of their interactions with adults has more depth and subtlety than before. They can be a pleasure to talk to, especially as their attitudes are generally unaffected by the preadolescent world-weariness that can sometimes taint Year 6 children. In terms of stages of learning, children in Year 5 are beginning to fan out across a wide field: some children will still need teaching at Year 4 or even Year 3 or Year 2 level and therefore the material prepared for those year groups may also be needed.

The National Curriculum, prescriptive though it may be, still involves making choices and because we cannot cover everything in a book such as this, we have relied heavily upon the schemes of work drawn up by the Qualifications and Curriculum Authority. These schemes are acknowledged as the basis for many school syllabuses so, with QCA guidelines to hand, we have tried to stick to the most obvious routes. We hope that you find this book particularly helpful when you are limited by time or have to meet the needs of voracious learners. Supply teachers and others 'caught on the hop' will also be able to rely on this material to help them to cope with demanding days.

Page	Activity	Objectives	Teachers' notes	NC, QCA & Primary Framework	Curriculum for Excellence (Scotland)	AT links and levels
15	Letter strings	To build independent spelling strategies by using common letter strings.	The strings are -ing, -ant, -ear and -ound. Children could record their sentences on the back of the sheet.	Literacy Strand 6 – Word structure and spelling	LIT 120X; LIT 220X – Tools for writing	AT3 Level 3/4
16	i before e!	To explore the spelling rule 'i before e except after c'.	Spelling books, word lists and dictionaries will be useful aids. Note that there are many exceptions to the rule.	Literacy Strand 6 – Word structure and spelling	LIT 120X; LIT 220X – Tools for writing	AT3 Level 3/4
17	Suffix towers	To build independent spelling strategies by using common suffixes.	Revise the meaning of the word 'suffix'.	Literacy Strand 6 – Word structure and spelling	LIT 220X – Tools for writing	AT3 Level 3/4
18	Homophones	To distinguish between homophones.	Answers are: pain/pane, pair/pear, sale/sail, bury/berry, thrown/throne, break/brake, ate/eight, plain/plane, hair/hare, stake/steak, rows/rose, prints/prince, stalk/stork, great/grate.	Literacy Strand 6 – Word structure and spelling	LIT 120X; LIT 220X – Tools for writing	AT3 Level 3/4
19	More than one: plurals (1)	To explore, collect and classify spelling patterns for pluralisations.	Each collection of words should conform to the same rule on pluralisation. The rule is clearly given with each set of words.	Literacy Strand 6 – Word structure and spelling	LIT 120X; LIT 220X – Tools for writing	AT3 Level 3/4
20	More than one: plurals (2)	To explore, collect and classify spelling patterns for pluralisations.	This sheet covers three new rules but follows the same pattern as the previous sheet.	Literacy Strand 6 – Word structure and spelling	LIT 120X; LIT 220X – Tools for writing	AT3 Level 4/5
21	Idiomatic phrases, clichés and expressions	To collect a range of idioms, clichés and expressions and to understand their meaning.	You might wish to explore the connection between the phrases and their original literal meaning.	Literacy Strand 7 – Understanding and interpreting texts	ENG 219V – Understanding, analysing and evaluating (reading)	AT2 Level 4
22	Prefixes	To explore and collect the spellings and meanings of words that begin with a prefix.	Children will need dictionaries and will need to know how to use one. A short revision of alphabetical order is worthwhile.	Literacy Strand 6 – Word structure and spelling	LIT 120X; LIT 220X – Tools for writing	AT2 Level 4
23	Onomatopoeia	To explore and collect onomatopoeic words and invent new words whose meaning is represented in sounds.	Demonstrate: bang on the table; clap your hands. The word 'onomatopoeia' is fun in itself; children should enjoy inventing new words as part of this sheet.	Literacy Strand 6 – Word structure and spelling	ENG 101A/L/W – Enjoyment and choice (writing) ENG 226AD – Creating texts	AT3 Level 4
24	All change (1)	To transform words by changing verbs to nouns using suffixes.	Adding suffixes often involves changes to the root word, hence 'pacifism' not 'pacifyism'. Can children suggest why the 'y' has been dropped? (A superfluous vowel sound.)	Literacy Strand 6 – Word structure and spelling	ENG 101A/L/W – Enjoyment and choice (reading) LIT 220X – Tools for writing	AT2 Level 2/3 AT3 Level 4
25	All change (2)	To transform words by changing verbs to nouns using suffixes.	An extension of work started on the previous sheet.	Literacy Strand 6 – Word structure and spelling	ENG 101A/L/W – Enjoyment and choice (reading) LIT 220X – Tools for writing	AT3 Level 4
26	Auxiliary verbs	To recognise how different tenses are formed using auxiliary verbs.	Note that underlining with colouring pencils is cheaper and less messy than highlighter pens. Revise what a verb is. The auxiliary verbs are: 1. could 2. has 3. will 4. may 5. were 6. was 7. was 8. shall 9. have 10. are.	Literacy Strand 11 – Sentence structure and punctuation	LIT 212N – Tools for reading	AT2 Level 4
27	From now to tomorrow	To explore how the future tense is formed using auxiliary verbs.	Answers are: 1. Flo will be a very good ballet dancer. 2. Raji will live in Solihull. 3. Arnold will be on holiday in Cyprus (or will be going to). 4. She will eat roast beef. 5. Mona will enjoy her skiing lessons. 6. Gandulf will become a very fat dog (or will be).	Literacy Strand 11 – Sentence structure and punctuation	LIT 212N – Tools for reading LIT 221Y – Tools for writing	AT2 Level 2 AT3 Level 4
28	From one person to another	To be able to identify examples of 1st, 2nd and 3rd person from reading.	Do not use this sheet: 'cold'; it's not an easy exercise. Answers are: 3rd person plural; 2nd person singular (it could be plural, but in this context there was only one!); 3rd person plural; 3rd person singular; 2nd person plural and 1st person singular.	Literacy Strand 11 – Sentence structure and punctuation	LIT 212N – Tools for reading	AT2 Level 4

SCHOLASTIC
www.scholastic.co.uk

Page	Activity	Objectives	Teachers' notes	NC, QCA & Primary Framework	Curriculum for Excellence (Scotland)	AT links and levels
29	Direct speech	To be able to recognise and write direct speech.	Give examples and teach where to place the punctuation in relation to the speech marks. Answers: 'Ding, dong!' chimed the clock. The Prince shouted, 'Don't go, Cinderella!' 'I never go to the Ball,' moaned the footman. 'I think that the Prince is very, very handsome,' twittered the bird. 'Am I really a pumpkin?' asked the coach. Cinderella said, 'I wish that I had worn my trainers'.	Literacy Strand 11 – Sentence structure and punctuation	LIT 212N – Tools for reading LIT 221Y; LIT 222Z – Tools for writing	AT3 Level 3/4
30	Direct speech – reported speech	To understand the difference between reported speech and direct speech. To write sentences using reported speech.	Allow small variations in the answers. Answers are: Cinderella wondered whether she should clean and cook or marry the Prince. The Ugly Sisters shouted at the Fairy Godmother to leave their pumpkins alone. The Fairy Godmother asked whether she should turn the Ugly Sisters into toads. The footman moaned that he did not have a Fairy Godmother.	Literacy Strand 11 – Sentence structure and organisation	LIT 212N – Tools for reading LIT 221Y; LIT 222Z – Tools for writing	AT3 Level 4/5
31	Directions for dialogue	To understand how dialogue is set out.	Reading this as a whole class is recommended. *Why do we need all this complicated punctuation?* Reiterate the rules and mark directly.	Literacy Strand 9 – Creating and shaping texts	LIT 212N – Tools for reading LIT 221Y; LIT 222Z – Tools for writing	AT3 Level 4/5
32	Writing a script	To be able to write a playscript applying conventions and adding production notes.	Without over-complicating explain a few simple rules: name who is speaking; use colons after names; add simple production notes (lighting, noises); scripts do not use speech marks. Show some examples to the class.	Literacy Strand 9 – Creating and shaping texts	LIT 221Y – Tools for writing LIT 225AC – Organising and using information ENG 230AH – Creating texts	AT3 Level 4
33	Writing for radio	To be able to write a playscript applying conventions and adding production notes.	Emphasise that the play is for radio. *What are the implications of this?* Get children to plan their script including a beginning, middle and end.	Literacy Strand 9 – Creating and shaping texts	LIT 221Y – Tools for writing LIT 225AC – Organising and using information ENG 230AH – Creating texts	AT3 Level 4
34	Points of view	To present a case, setting down arguments as bullet points.	Show children documents containing bullet points, if available. This sheet contains information but no single point of view. Explain what they need to do. They may go beyond the given information if they have additional relevant points to make.	Literacy Strand 7 – Understanding and interpreting texts	LIT 221Y – Tools for writing LIT 225AC; ENG 229AG – Organising and using information LIT 228AF – Creating texts	AT2 Level 4/5 AT3 Level 4
35	Persuasive devices	To collect and explore the use of persuasive devices.	This sheet will need explanation. You might use the sheet over a period of time (say a week) and get children to watch out for other examples of persuasive devices.	Literacy Strand 7 – Understanding and interpreting texts	LIT 218U – Understanding, analysing and evaluating (reading)	AT2 Level 4
36	Getting it wrong	To investigate ambiguities that arise from contracted sentences.	Children need to understand the jokes and the meaning of the word 'ambiguous'. Explain that it is the shortening of sentences and phrases that gives rise to the ambiguities.	Literacy Strand 7 – Understanding and interpreting texts	LIT 218U – Understanding, analysing and evaluating (reading)	AT2 Level 3/4
37	A pile of prepositions	To identify prepositions and to understand and use the term.	Explain that the 'prepositions' describe the relationship between nouns and pronouns: the preposition 'under' tells us the relationship between 'bone' and 'chair'. Answers are: **1.** off **2.** in **3.** towards **4.** over **5.** down **6.** against **7.** through **8.** to **9.** behind.	Literacy Strand 11 – Sentence structure and punctuation	LIT 212N – Tools for reading	AT2 Level 4
38	I protest!	To write a letter to protest or put forward a point of view.	Show a few genuine examples of letters demonstrating the conventions involved. Modern letters written by the 'computer generation' tend to have fewer full-stops and the text therefore has a cleaner less cluttered look than before.	Literacy Strand 7 – Understanding and interpreting texts; Strand 9 – Creating and shaping texts	LIT 218U – Understanding, analysing and evaluating (reading)	AT2 Level 4/5 AT3 Level 3/4
39	Taking temperatures	To read temperature scales accurately (including negative numbers). To read and write symbols relating to measuring temperature.	Check that children know how to read a scale (every degree is marked). Answers are: **1a.** 2°C **1b.** –6°C **1c.** –15°C **1d.** 14°C **1e.** 12°C **2.** (in order): –15°C, –6°C, 2°C, 12°C, 14°C **3.** 29°C **4.** 8° **5.** 6°C **6.** 10°C.	Maths Strand – Measuring	MNU 218M – Measurement	AT3 Level 3/4
40	All square	To be able to recognise square numbers and relate to drawings of squares.	Demonstrate by starting the grid on a board. The table will show all the square numbers from 1² to 10². Answers are: 1, 4, 9, 16, 25, 36, 49, 64, 81, 100. Other answers are: 81, 81m², 25.	Maths Strand – Knowing and using number facts	MTH 221P – Patterns and relationships	AT2 Level 4

Page	Activity	Objectives	Teachers' notes	NC, QCA & Primary Framework	Curriculum for Excellence (Scotland)	AT links and levels
41	For every…	To be able to solve word problems involving ratio and proportion.	This sheet introduces the common language of 'ratio' so it is worth doing a number of similar questions orally with the class. Answers are: 62, 2, 10, 8, 15, 24.	Maths Strands – Using and applying mathematics; Counting and understanding number	MNU 203C – Addition, subtraction, multiplication and division	AT1 Level 3/4 AT2 Level 4
42	Decimals, fractions and percentages	To be able to recognise the equivalence between percentages, fractions and decimals and to identify a percentage of a shape.	Prior knowledge is assumed. Answers are: **a.** 25% **b.** 20% **c.** 10% **d.** 50% **e.** 75% **f.** 50% **g.** 50% **h.** 75%.	Maths Strand – Counting and understanding number	MNU 209H – Fractions, decimals and percentages	AT2 Level 4
43	Leftovers	To understand the idea of a remainder and to begin to give a quotient as a fraction when dividing by a whole number.	How we deal with remainders needs to be taught. Note that sometimes we ignore it: 13 children divided into two teams is not $6\frac{1}{2}$ children. Answers are: **a.** $4\frac{1}{8}$ **b.** $5\frac{5}{6}$ **c.** $9\frac{4}{5}$ **d.** $12\frac{1}{6}$ **e.** $2\frac{4}{7}$ **f.** $6\frac{3}{4}$ **g.** $4\frac{7}{8}$ **h.** $12\frac{1}{5}$. Answers to the problems are: **1.** 7 boxes **2.** 4 coaches **3.** 5 tickets.	Maths Strand – Calculating	MNU 209H – Estimation and rounding	AT2 Level 4
44	Estimate and calculate	To develop mental calculation strategies and to begin to use a calculator effectively.	Encourage children to develop strategies that will help them arrive at sensible answers (not guesses). For example, in question 1, (5 × 5), the last digit of the answer must be 5 because 5 × 5 = 25. Therefore 2775 must be the correct answer. Answers are: **1.** 2775 **2.** 2592 **3.** 8982 **4.** 64 **5.** 45 **6.** 25 **7.** 378 **8.** 868 **9.** 1558 **10.** 36 **11.** 24. **12.** 17 **13.** 3960 **14.** 3124 **15.** 2890 **16** 24 **17.** 64 **18.** 62 **19.** 8281 **20.** 3198 **21.** 5115.	Maths Strand – Calculating	MNU 201A – Estimation and rounding	AT2 Level 4
45	Hot shot!	To begin to use a calculator effectively. To reinforce understanding of place value.	Subtracting each digit requires an understanding of HTU place value. Children will get plenty of practice using a calculator.	Maths Strand – Calculating	MNU 202B – Number processes	AT2 Level 4
46	Polyominoes	To be able to solve mathematical problems or puzzles. To identify and explain patterns and relationships. To generalise and predict.	Establish the rules: edge fully to edge, rotations and flip-overs are not new arrangements. Use squared paper or apparatus to aid the problem solving. 12 of the pentominoes, when laid out, approximate to the letters F, L, I, P, S, T, U, V, W, X, Y, Z.	Maths Strands – Using and applying mathematics; Understanding shape	MTH 120S; MTH 223S – Properties of 2D shapes and 3D objects	AT1 Level 3 AT3 Level 3
47	It's a problem (1)	To be able to use all four operations to solve word problems involving numbers based on 'real life'.	Demonstrate how to solve a similar problem 'out loud'. Get some children to do the same and focus on the processes used. Answers are: **1.** one hour and 35 minutes **2.** two hours and 20 minutes **3.** 213 miles **4.** 378 miles.	Maths Strands – Using and applying mathematics; Measuring	MNU 103; MNU 203C – Addition, subtraction, multiplication and division	AT1 Level 3/4
48	It's a problem (2)	To be able to use all four operations to solve word problems involving numbers based on 'real life'.	Answers are: **1.** 35.2kg **2.** £13 **3a.** £204 **3b.** £43.25 **3c.** £64 **3d.** £4.80 **3e.** £66.50 **3f.** £36 **4.** Yes, they can all go. (They can take 85 people legally.)	Maths Strand – Using and applying mathematics	MNU 103; MNU 203C – Addition, subtraction, multiplication and division	AT1 Level 3/4
49	Know your measures	To be able to use language and abbreviations related to measures. To know relationships between familiar units. To know the names of commonly used imperial units.	Preface with a short lesson about different systems of measures. Think of examples, such as, 6 feet tall, 100mph. Answers are: distance, capacity, capacity; **1.** 4.74m **2.** 32.51m **3.** 1.41 **4.** 5.5l **5.** 4.3kg **6.** 6.5kg.	Maths Strand – Measuring	MNU 218M – Measurement	AT3 Level 3
50	Using the right measure	To be able to suggest suitable units to estimate or measure length, mass or capacity. To record readings from scales accurately	Accept reasonable answers in the boxes (you wouldn't measure a fish in miles). Answers for second section are: **a.** 360ml **b.** 460ml **c.** 430ml.	Maths Strand – Measuring	MNU 218M – Measurement	AT3 Level 3
51	Calculating areas	To be able to calculate the area of rectangles.	The drawings are scaled down. Encourage children to show their thinking on paper. Answers are: **a.** $12m^2$ **b.** $11m^2$ **c.** $5m^2$ **d.** $48cm^2$ **e.** $25cm^2$ **f.** $48cm^2$ **g.** $13cm^2$ **h.** $28cm^2$ **I.** $16cm^2$.	Maths Strand – Measuring	MNU 219M – Measurement	AT3 Level 4/5
52	Area and perimeter	To be able to measure and calculate the area and perimeter of simple shapes.	Areas are: T = $26cm^2$, V = $33cm^2$, E = $40cm^2$; H = $46cm^2$. Perimeters are: T = 30cm, V = 36cm, E = 44cm, H = 50cm.	Maths Strand – Measuring	MNU 219M – Measurement	AT3 Level 4
53	The right time	To be able to read the time using timetables and to be able to understand and use that information.	Revise the 24-hour clock. Answers are: **1.** 32 minutes; **2.** 05:33 from Oxford; **3.** 10:27; **4.** four trains (the 09:51 doesn't run on Saturdays; **5.** no.	Maths Strand – Measuring	MNU 214L – Time	AT3 Level 3/4

Page	Activity	Objectives	Teachers' notes	NC, QCA & Primary Framework	Curriculum for Excellence (Scotland)	AT links and levels
54	Missing links	To identify 2D shapes from their descriptions.	This is straightforward. Mark by visual reference.	Maths Strand – Understanding shape	MTH 119S; MTH 223S – Properties of 2D shapes and 3D objects	AT3 Level 3
55	Making reflections	To be able to recognise reflective symmetry in 2D shapes, reflections and translations.	Use prepared shapes and mirrors to investigate the number of axes of reflective symmetry in regular and irregular polygons. (Paper shapes can also be folded to check for the axes.)	Maths Strand – Understanding shape	MTH 123V; MTH 231V – Angles, symmetry and transformation	AT3 Level 3/4
56	Coordinated shapes	To be able to read and plot points using coordinates in the first quadrant.	Revise how to plot coordinates first. The two shapes to be plotted on the grid are an oblong and an isosceles triangle.	Maths Strand – Understanding shape	MTH 230U – Angles, symmetry and transformation	AT3 Level 3/4
57	Measurement by degrees	To be able to measure and calculate acute, obtuse and right angles using a protractor. To calculate angles in a straight line.	Decent protractors are required. Demonstrate how to use one. Stress that the angles at the bottom of the page are calculated not measured. Answers are: **1.** 132° **2.** 57° **3.** 113° **4.** 28° **5.** 75° **6.** 145° **7.** 104° **8.** 90° **9.** 135° **10.** 158° **11.** 60°.	Maths Strand – Understanding shape	MTH 227T – Angles, symmetry and transformation	AT3 Level 4/5
58	Know your angles	To classify angles and to know associated vocabulary.	This is a cut-and-paste operation that can be marked by visual reference.	Maths Strand – Understanding shape	MTH 226T – Angles, symmetry and transformation	AT3 Level 4/5
59	Accident and Emergency graph	To extract and interpret data from graphs.	Check that the terminology is known. Allow some leeway in the answers. The number of patients treated is 44, 54, 30, 44, 70, 87, 73, 60, 43, 62. Answers are: **1.** 567 **2.** 44 **3.** 87 **4.** one day (14.01) **5.** A good guess is the weekend; sports matches, DIY and closed GP surgeries may account for more self-referrals to casualty.	Maths Strand – Handling data	MNU 232W – Data and analysis	AT1 Level 3/4 AT4 Level 4
60	Milkman's maths: line graph	To develop an understanding of mode and range. To draw and interpret a line graph.	Note the need to be able to estimate the position of 13 and 9 on this graph. Answers are: the mode is 16; the range is 14. The last answer is open-ended.	Maths Strand – Handling data	MNU 232W; MTH 234X – Data and analysis	AT1 Level 3/4 AT4 Level 4
61	Healthy connections	To understand that to stay healthy we need an adequate and varied diet.	Obesity is a major threat to health but try not to worry children about their body image. The obesity problem is the responsibility of adults, not children. Answers are: scurvy – fed them limes (hence 'limeys'); rickets – fed them cod-liver oil etc; death of babies – fed them potatoes etc. In Paris, lower class babies ate potatoes and gravy containing some vitamin C.	Science NC: Sc1 Ideas and evidence in science; Sc2 Humans and other animals QCA: Unit 5A Keeping healthy	SCN 225M – Keeping my body healthy	AT1 Level 3 AT2 Level 3
62	Trace a torso: the heart and lungs	To know that the heart and lungs are protected by the ribs and that the muscle in the walls of the heart contracts regularly to pump blood around the body.	It is recommended that you provide ready-cut rectangles of tracing paper to avoid waste. Answers are: **1.** the heart and lungs are protected by the ribs **2.** the muscle in the wall of the heart contracts to pump blood around the body.	Science NC: SC2 Humans and other animals QCA: Unit 5A Keeping healthy	SCN 111M – Keeping my body healthy	AT2 Level 4
63	Seed dispersal	To learn that seeds can be dispersed in a variety of ways.	Ideally use this sheet in autumn. Dispersion takes place in many ways. Answers are: Water – coconut, mangrove. Wind: dandelion, ash tree, sycamore. Explosion: cucumbers (some explode to hurl seeds around). Animal: rose-hip, blackberry.	Science NC: Sc2 Green plants QCA: Unit 5B Life cycles	SCN 208B – Biodiversity	AT2 Level 3/4
64	Pollination	To understand that plants produce flowers which have male and female organs and that insects pollinate some flowers.	Spring is a good time to use this sheet as you can observe real plants. Other pollination methods are wind, water and human intervention (plant nurseries for example).	Science NC: Sc2 Green plants QCA: Unit 5B Life cycles	SCN 208B – Biodiversity	AT1 Level 3 AT2 Level 4/5
65	Guess the gas	To know that air has weight and it is all around us and that there are many gases some of which are important to us.	Start with class discussion and plenty of reference material. Answers are: for a manned balloon (helium); in fizzy drink (CO_2); gas fire (natural gas); hospital (oxygen). Possible answers to the last part are: scuba-diving; using a camping stove.	Science NC: SC3 Grouping and classifying materials QCA: Unit 5D Changing state	SCN 115X – Properties and uses	AT3 Level 4
66	Solids, liquids and gases	To understand how gases are different from solids and liquids.	Gases flow more easily than liquids and are more easily squashed than liquids or solids. When liquids are released from containers they run along the floor; gases flow everywhere.	Science NC: SC3 Grouping and classifying materials QCA: Unit 5D Changing state	SCN 115X – Properties and uses	AT3 Level 4

Page	Activity	Objectives	Teachers' notes	NC, QCA & Primary Framework	Curriculum for Excellence (Scotland)	AT links and levels
67	Changing state: evaporation	To understand that evaporation is when a liquid turns into a gas.	During evaporation, a liquid does not disappear but it changes to a gas. We smell odours because gases enter our noses. Safety: be aware of problems related to the use of solvents like nail varnish.	Science NC: SC3 Changing materials QCA: Unit 5D Changing state	SCN 233Z – Chemical reactions	AT3 Level 4/5
68	Changing state: condensation	To understand that condensation is when a gas turns to a liquid.	Demonstrate condensation by covering a container that contains hot water in cling film. Put an ice cube on top of the cling film. When water vapour cools down it returns to a liquid state.	Science NC: SC3 Changing materials QCA: Unit 5D Changing state	SCN 233Z – Chemical reactions	AT3 Level 4/5
69	The water cycle	To understand the water cycle in terms of the processes involved.	This topic should be dealt with after children have studied both condensation and evaporation.	Science NC: SC3 Changing materials QCA: Unit 5D Changing state	SCN 203A – Planet Earth	AT3 Level 4 AT4 Level 3/4
70	Heavens above!	To understand some key facts about the Sun, Earth and Moon (relative size, Earth's rotation, night and day).	Each pair will need a torch, a globe, beach ball (Sun), a dried pea (Earth) and a tiny bead half the size of the pea (Moon). The Sun is around 389 times further away from the Earth than the Moon is.	Science NC: Sc4 The Earth and beyond QCA: Unit 5E Earth, Sun and Moon	SCN 213E – Astronomy	AT4 Level 4/5
71	The Moon's orbit	To know that the Moon takes approximately 28 days to orbit the Earth and that the different appearances of the Moon provide evidence for the 28-day cycle.	Note that the period of the Moon's revolution around the Earth is 27.3 days but, because of the Earth's progress around the Sun, the Sun's light strikes at a slightly different angle by the end of the month; we see the phase repeat every 29.5 days.	Science NC: Sc4 The Earth and beyond QCA: Unit 5E Earth, Sun and Moon	SCN 213E – Astronomy	AT4 Level 4/5
72	Vibrations	To understand that sounds are produced when objects vibrate.	Some demonstration that sound is caused by vibration should precede this sheet, for example, dried peas bouncing on a drum.	Science NC: Sc4 Light and sound QCA: Unit 5F Changing sounds	SCN 231W – Sound	AT4 Level 4/5
73	Metronome muffling	To understand that some materials are more effective than others in preventing sound from reaching the ear.	This is not suitable for whole-class work. Discuss the issue of 'fair testing' before the children begin. *How can you be fair about judging the loudness of the sound heard?*	Science NC: Sc4 Light and sound QCA: Unit 5F Changing sounds	SCN 231W – Sound	AT4 Level 4/5
74	Changing pitch: wind instruments	To understand that sounds can be made by air vibrating and to understand how the pitch of the sound can be altered. To test this knowledge practically.	Blow across the mouth of a bottle to demonstrate how a wind instrument works. *What is vibrating to cause the sound?* Add water to the bottle for variation. A plastic hose, 12mm to 16mm diameter, is needed to make the pan pipe.	Science NC: Sc4 Light and sound QCA: Unit 5F Changing sounds	SCN 231W – Sound	AT4 Level 4/5
75	Changing pitch: stringed instruments	To understand that the pitch of a stringed instrument depends upon the length, thickness and tightness of the string. To test this knowledge practically.	At least two children are required for this activity. You could provide more than two thicknesses of string, but don't make it too complicated; there are already three variables. The instruments are in size order, which is also pitch order (violin, viola, cello and double bass).	Science NC: Sc4 Light and sound QCA: Unit 5F Changing sounds	SCN 231W – Sound	AT4 Level 4/5
76	Banging on	To understand that the pitch of a drum depends upon its size and the tightness of its skin.	At a suitable time children should experiment with playing a range of drums. The pitch of the drums falls broadly in order of size: kettle drum, tenor drum, side drum and tom-tom.	Science NC: Sc4 Light and sound QCA: Unit 5F Changing sounds	SCN 231W – Sound	AT4 Level 4/5
77	Images of a queen: Victoria	To identify Queen Victoria, facts about her life and the period in which she lived.	Address any unfamiliar words, such as, 'population'. Children might make a presentation about Queen Victoria using ICT.	History NC: Chronological understanding; Victorian Britain QCA: Unit 11 What was it like for children living in Victorian Britain?	SOC 104E; SOC 204E – People, past events and societies	AT 3/4
78	Victorian people who made history (1)	To collect information from a range of sources about important Victorian figures in Victorian times. To understand that the work of individuals can change aspects of society.	Treat as a detective exercise. Children might interrogate the clues in small groups and back this up with investigative work using books and ICT. Note that the children are to research the seventh Earl of Cardigan.	History NC: Historical enquiry; Victorian Britain QCA: Unit 11 What was it like for children living in Victorian Britain?	SOC 103C; SOC 204E – People, past events and societies	AT Level 4/5
79	Victorian people who made history (2)	To collect information from a range of sources and to find out about important figures in Victorian times. To understand that the work of individuals can change aspects of society.	Work through this as on the previous sheet.	History NC: Historical enquiry; Victorian Britain QCA: Unit 11 What was it like for children living in Victorian Britain?	SOC 104E; SOC 204E – People, past events and societies	AT Level 4/5

NO FUSS
PHOTOCOPIABLE

■SCHOLASTIC
www.scholastic.co.uk

Page	Activity	Objectives	Teacher's notes	NC, QCA & Primary Framework	Curriculum for Excellence (Scotland)	AT links and levels
80	Poor children at work	To understand a number of aspects of daily life for poor Victorian children.	Let children work in groups and list all the facts given in evidence. Note that the inspectors quoted extensively from interviews with children and others.	History NC: Historical enquiry; Victorian Britain QCA: Unit 11 What was it like for children living in Victorian Britain?	SOC 203C; SOC 204E– People, past events and societies	AT Level 4/5
81	Timeline of change: Victorian schools	To use a timeline to recap the main events, dates and figures and to help recall some of the main changes in the lives of children during the Victorian period.	There are enough clues for this to be a fairly straightforward exercise. Children should study a real Victorian school building if they can – there are plenty about!	History NC: Chronological understanding; Historical enquiry; Victorian Britain QCA: Unit 11 What was it like for children living in Victorian Britain?	SOC 203C; SOC 201A; SOC 204E – People, past events and societies	AT Level 4
82	Decade decisions	To place pictures in the correct decade on a post-war timeline. To recognise some differences between now and then.	Use different colours to differentiate the decades. Answers are: 1950s = Teddy boy, Queen Elizabeth's coronation, ration book, Morris Minor, Bush TV; 1960s = Record – *Music to twist to*, Mods on Lambrettas. 1940s = Anderson shelter, gas mask.	History NC: Chronological understanding; Britain since 1930 QCA: Unit 13 How has life changed since 1948?	SOC 203C; SOC 201A – People, past events and societies	AT Level 3/4
83	Changing faces: immigration	To communicate understanding of changes that have happened to the British way of life since 1948.	Children should notice that: 1. They all appear to be West Indian. 2. Men predominate. 3. They are wearing suits. 4. Hats are worn by some of them. You should discuss the answers. *What would these people have noticed as different from their homeland?*	History NC: Historical enquiry; Britain since 1930 QCA: Unit 13 How has life changed since 1948?	SOC 201A; SOC 202B; SOC 203C – People, past events and societies	AT Level 4
84	1950s' money	To look in detail at one change in an aspect of life in Britain since 1948.	Show real money if you can. Use the chart as a place value grid, that is, move into the 'shillings' column if number of pence is 12 or over. Answers for the cost of each item are: milk = 1/6d (1 shilling 6 pence); potatoes =10d (10 pence); eggs = 4/- (4 shillings); flour = 1/- (1 shilling). Total cost = 7/4d (seven shillings and four pence – approximately 37p).	History NC: Historical enquiry; Britain since 1930 QCA: Unit 15 How has life changed since 1948?	SOC 201A; SOC 203C – People, past events and societies	AT Level 4/5
85	Wet and dry map	To identify wet and dry areas of the world on a map, using atlases and other sources of information as an aid.	Check that your atlases are up to date and revise the skills needed to use one. You will find the *Guinness Book of Records* useful in a plenary session. *Where is the driest place on Earth?*	Geography NC: Geographical enquiry and skills; Knowledge and understanding of places QCA: Unit 11 Water	SOC 111J; SOC 212J; SOC 214L – People, place and environment	AT Level 4
86	What use is water?	To understand how water is used.	This sheet is about collecting and organising data. You might choose to look at water usage within school only.	Geography NC: Knowledge and understanding of patterns and processes QCA: Unit 11 Water	SOC 213K – People in society, economy and business	AT Level 4/5
87	From reservoir to tap: from dirty to clean	To carry out an experiment to observe how water is cleaned.	Ideally you should visit a water treatment plant. The experiment is a cooperative activity. Supervise closely – children should not drink the water.	Geography NC: Geographical enquiry and skills; Knowledge and understanding of patterns and processes QCA: Unit 11 Water	SOC 118R – People in society, economy and business	AT Level 3/4
88	Water costs money	To understand about water bills and the problems associated with the notion of owning water.	The notion that water has to be paid for may come as news to many of the children. Links can easily be made between this sheet and Citizenship as well as to conservation.	Geography NC: Geographical enquiry and skills; Knowledge and understanding of patterns and processes QCA: Unit 11 Water	SOC 222S – People in society, economy and business	AT Level 3/4
89	Coastal zones	To identify coastal features using maps. To use appropriate geographical terminology.	You might provide detailed maps of a coastline near to you. Examples of soft and hard rock for the children to examine would be an asset. This may fit well with a field study project.	Geography NC: Geographical enquiry and skills QCA: Unit 23 Investigating coasts	SOC 113K; SOC 213K – People, place and environment	AT Level 3/4
90	Erosion	To identify erosion landforms and to understand the impact that human activity may have on coastal environments.	Answers are: 1. arch 2. stack 3. cave. Human activity answers might include building, road construction, walking, climbing, mineral extraction and fossil hunting.	Geography NC: Geographical enquiry and skills QCA: Unit 23 Investigating coasts	SOC 113K – People, place and environment	AT Level 3/4
91	The beach	To learn about the different types of beach and identify them using keys. To understand the impact humans have on coastal areas.	Colouring pencils are required. The symbols used for sand and shingle are found on Ordnance Survey® maps.	Geography NC: Geographical enquiry and skills QCA: Unit 23 Investigating coasts	SOC 113K; SOC 213K – People, place and environment	AT Level 3/4

Page	Activity	Objectives	Teachers' notes	NC, QCA & Primary Framework	Curriculum for Excellence (Scotland)	AT links and levels
92	We do like to be beside the seaside	To use maps and secondary sources to research and describe an area of coast suitable for a particular type of holiday.	You will need to decide how large a task you wish this sheet to be – it could turn into a major art, craft or ICT project. Discuss the holiday types and unfamiliar words like 'itinerary'.	Geography NC: Geographical enquiry and skills QCA: Unit 23 Investigating coasts	SOC 113K; SOC 213K – People, place and environment	AT Level 3/4
93	Structures (1): striking sounds	To understand how different instruments work. To produce a quality percussion instrument that will produce a series of controllable sounds when played. To join and combine materials and components accurately.	Experimenting with a range of musical instruments is a prerequisite for this activity. Materials will be needed to complete the task.	Design and technology NC: Knowledge and understanding of materials and components; Working with tools, equipment, materials and components to make quality products QCA: Unit 5A Musical instruments	TCH 207D – Technologies	AT Level 3
94	Structures (2): tunes from tubes	To understand how different instruments work. To produce a quality wind instrument that will play a series of controllable sounds. To join and combine materials and components accurately.	Revise how a sound is produced by a wind instrument. Note that children should not be encouraged to share instruments that are placed in mouths. Sterilise tubes with mild antiseptic.	Design and technology NC: Working with tools, equipment, materials and components to make quality products; Knowledge and understanding of materials and components QCA: Unit 5A Musical instruments	TCH 207D – Technologies	AT Level 3
95	Using your loaf	To understand that there are a wide variety of breads and bread products. To work safely and hygienically, weighing and measuring accurately, to produce bread.	Discuss bread and bread products and variations across the world in bread types. Bread making by children themselves is an activity that needs special management.	Design and technology NC: Working with tools, equipment, materials and components to make quality products; Knowledge and understanding of materials and components QCA: Unit 5B Bread	TCH 207D – Technologies	AT Level 3/4
96	Mechanisms (1): moving along	To recognise a cam within a mechanism and how it changes movement. To understand that a cam changes rotary motion into linear motion.	Children should examine a range of toys that use a cam. Consult your DT subject leader. Check and monitor that the equipment is used with care. Life is not risk free and even glue guns present some hazards.	Design and technology NC: Working with tools, equipment, materials and components to make quality products; Knowledge and understanding of materials and components QCA: Unit 5C Moving toys	TCH 207D; TCH 205C – Technologies	AT Level 3/4
97	Mechanisms (2): moving around	To recognise a cam within a mechanism and how it changes movement. To understand that a cam changes rotary motion into linear motion. To understand that different shaped cams produce different movements.	As above, except this time we are focusing on movement being produced by different cams. Explaining 'out loud' is a good way to test understanding – even your own.	Design and technology NC: Working with tools, equipment, materials and components to make quality products; Knowledge and understanding of materials and components QCA: Unit 5C Moving toys	TCH 207D; TCH 205C – Technologies	AT Level 3/4
98	Manipulating models	To use an object-based graphics package to manipulate shapes.	This work demands an object-based computer software package.	ICT NC: Developing ideas and making things happen QCA: Unit 5A Graphical modelling	TCH 209E – Technologies	AT Level 3
99	Spreadsheet scoreboard	To enter data into cells on a spreadsheet, modify data and check results.	Remind children how to enter data on a spreadsheet; they will need to be able to enter data and label columns and rows. Demonstrate the short way of making totals using 'autosum' and how to calculate averages using 'average' (from the 'autosum' drop-down menu. Answers are: Dravid (best average 75.7); Second Test (highest total score of 268 runs). Yes. If the error was corrected Ganguly would have the highest average (91.7).	ICT NC: Finding things out; Developing ideas and making things happen QCA: Unit 5D Introduction to spreadsheets	TCH 318H – Technologies	AT Level 4
100	The cheapest school trip	To create and use a spreadsheet to calculate costs.	This sheet is for competent spreadsheet users. Travel costs should be worked out in £ not p. Norfolk is the cheapest trip (£98.33 per child); Broadstairs the most expensive (£140.70 per child); Hotel costs are the most significant factor but which trip children choose may be justified in various ways.	ICT NC: Finding things out; Developing ideas and making things happen QCA: Unit 5D Introduction to spreadsheets	TCH 318H – Technologies	AT Level 4/5
101	Controlling devices	To recognise that control technology is all around us and that devices can be controlled through direct instruction.	*What are controlling devices? What do we mean by a sequence of instructions?* Examples of other devices might include burglar alarms, car door locks and cooker timers.	ICT NC: Developing ideas and making things happen QCA: Unit 5E Controlling devices	TCH 216K – Technologies	AT Level 4

Page	Activity	Objectives	Teacher's notes	NC, QCA & Primary Framework	Curriculum for Excellence (Scotland)	AT links and levels
102	Taking control	To understand that control box software can be used to control an output device.	The sheet illustrates one set-up using a control device. Yours may vary but the basic principles do not change. Children's work should begin with connecting the bulb to the control box. You should make all connections before they start. This is self-marking: either the procedure does what it should or it doesn't..	ICT NC: Developing ideas and making things happen QCA: Unit 5E Controlling devices	TCH 216K – Technologies	AT Level 4
103	Controlling traffic lights	To use simple control language to activate multiple devices concurrently.	Demonstrate how a traffic light system can be constructed. Children can then concentrate on writing the control language. (Note that 'SWITCH OFF 3 2' is not 'SWITCH OFF 32'.)	ICT NC: Developing ideas and making things happen QCA: Unit 5E Controlling devices	TCH 216K – Technologies	AT Level 4
104	Still life (1)	To compare and comment on ideas, methods and approaches used in still-life paintings.	This sheet and the next need to be 'talked through' and accompanied by lots of investigation of paintings. Visit galleries or their websites. Confirm that children understand the terms 'technique', 'contrast', 'composition', 'line' and 'texture'.	Art and design NC: Exploring and developing ideas; Evaluating and developing work QCA: Unit 5A Objects and meanings	EXA 204C – Art and Design	AT Level 4
105	Still life (2)	To compare and comment on ideas, methods and approaches used in still-life paintings.	This is a companion to the last sheet. (See previous notes.) The answer to the first question is 'still life'.	Art and design NC: Exploring and developing ideas; Evaluating and developing work QCA: Unit 5A Objects and meanings	EXA 204C – Art and Design	AT Level 4
106	Still life DIY	To select and record a still life from first-hand observation. To make a number of small studies that explore different ideas.	You should manage this so that only small groups reach the painting stage at any one time. Provide a few decorative or interesting additions to the classroom setting if you can: an unusual vase, drapes or flowers.	Art and design NC: Investigating and making art, craft and design QCA: Unit 5A Objects and meaning	EXA 208G – Art and Design	AT Level 4
107	Urn, vessel, basket and pot	To explore the tradition of making containers. To consider the work of contemporary designers of vessels. To create and decorate a container.	Let children examine a range of containers from pictures and around the classroom. Explore www.craftscouncil.org.uk, www.britishmuseum.ac.uk or www.caa.org.uk. The missing words are 'container' and 'contemporary'.	Art and design NC: Exploring and developing ideas; Evaluating and developing work QCA: Unit 5B Containers	EXA 208G – Art and Design	AT Level 4
108	Textile tales	To identify and comment on the content, ideas and ways that stories are communicated visually using textiles.	Either before or after using this sheet look at illustrations in a variety of forms. An example of a textile picture that can be handled and examined closely would be a bonus.	Art and design NC: Exploring and developing ideas; Evaluating and developing work	EXA 208G; EXA 209H – Art and Design	AT Level 4/5
109	Tell a terrible tale in textiles	To make a collaborative textile work that tells a story.	This is not a small scale project. It can prove to be most rewarding but it will need planning and some research. You will also need materials and to talk about the techniques that you might use. Tell the story of Cyclops first.	Art and design NC: Exploring and developing ideas; Knowledge and understanding QCA: Unit 5C Talking textiles	EXA 208G; EXA 209H – Art and Design	AT Level 4/5
110	Space odyssey	To identify contrasting moods and sensations and to explore different sound textures.	You may wish to limit this to untuned instruments. You could also demonstrate the type of sounds described. Children may add their own words to those on the sheet.	Music NC: Creating and developing musical ideas; Responding and reviewing QCA: Unit 18 Journey into space…	EXA 214Q – Music	AT Level 3/4
111	Harmony or agony?	To explore the effects of different combinations of pitched notes using appropriate language.	Demonstrate the value of harmony by playing the harmony to a song or hymn minus the melody, and vice versa. Children can do the activity unaided but singing the scale as a class is a good idea.	Music NC: Creating and developing musical ideas QCA: Unit 17 Roundabout; Unit 18 Journey into space…	EXA 214Q – Music	AT Level 4
112	Send round a fireman	To sing a simple round in two parts and accompany it with a three-note chord (triad).	Music making is often a social activity – you cannot sing a round on your own. Teach the round. A piano accompaniment is not essential. Children need to practise the playing of the chord to a steady pulse (the first beat in every bar or beats 1 and 3).	Music NC: Controlling sounds through singing and playing QCA: Unit 17 Roundabout	EXA 214Q – Music	AT Level 4
113	Ostinato, drone and melody	To accompany a round with repeated chords and ostinati.	Playing the same chord over and over again is a drone; a constantly repeated sequence of notes is an ostinato. 'Walk' is used as shorthand for a crotchet and 'run-ning' for a quaver. Answers are: **1.** drone **2.** ostinato **3.** ostinato **4.** ostinato **5.** ostinato **6.** drone **7.** drone.	Music NC: Controlling sounds through singing and playing QCA: Unit 17 Roundabout	EXA 214Q – Music	AT Level 4

Page	Activity	Objectives	Teachers' notes	NC, QCA & Primary Framework	Curriculum for Excellence (Scotland)	AT links and levels
114	Open and closed	To identify and control different ways in which percussion instruments make sounds.	Make sure that the two types of sound are demonstrated. Children should describe the method by which they produced the two types of sound on the instruments that they used.	Music NC: Responding and reviewing QCA: Unit 18 Journey into space...	EXA 214Q – Music	AT Level 4
115	Keeping the pulse	To improvise rhythmic patterns to a steady pulse.	Practise repeating rhythmic patterns to a steady pulse. For example, clap and say a four-beat pulse... Who is in class? Point to 'Emma'. The class reply (while you continue clapping or beating the pulse) Em-ma is in class and so on.	Music NC: Creating and developing musical ideas: Listening, and applying knowledge and understanding QCA: Unit 16 Cyclic patterns	EXA 214Q – Music	AT Level 3/4
116	Islam: key words	To identify basic religious beliefs of Muslims about Allah, Muhammad and the Qur'an (Koran).	This sheet should be used in the context of a wider project on Islam which you should not plunge into without being confident in your own knowledge of the subject.	RE Non-statutory framework: Learning about religion QCA: Unit 5A Why is Muhammad important to Muslims?		Non-statutory AT1 Level 3/4
117	Five pillars	To identify the five pillars of Islam.	The sheet focuses on fact rather than faith and you will need books and resources to support the work.	RE Non-statutory framework: Learning about religion QCA: Unit 5B How do Muslims express their beliefs...?		Non-statutory AT1 Level 3/4
118	Pilgrimage	To know the events and purpose of the Hajj and to understand the difference between a pilgrimage and an ordinary journey.	Discuss different pilgrimages (an external journey to meet an internal need, is one definition). Think of Lourdes, Graceland, Auschwitz.	RE Non-statutory framework: Learning about religion QCA: Unit 5B How do Muslims express their beliefs...?		Non-statutory AT1 Level 4
119	A special book	To know that the Bible is the world's best-selling book. To be able to place some events relating to it on a timeline. To be able to differentiate dates before and after Jesus.	The Bible is the world's best-selling book; discuss the reasons for this. Children should be familiar with the system of dating (AD precedes the year number; BC follows it.)	RE Non-statutory framework: Learning about religion; Breadth of study (Religions and beliefs; Themes) QCA: Unit 5C Where did the Christian Bible come from?		Non-statutory AT1 Level 4
120	Belief and action	To identify the link between belief and action and to think about how Christians might apply their beliefs in practical situations.	This sheet would match well with any activities related to Christian Aid Week when you could focus on local events and local charities.	RE Non-statutory framework: Learning from religion QCA: Unit 5D How do the beliefs of Christians influence...?		Non-statutory AT2 Level 3/4
121	Love your neighbour	To understand why Christians see all people as neighbours and to begin to understand that stories contain meaning beyond the literal.	Find and read the story. (The Good News Bible is widely accepted as a child-friendly version of the Bible.) The captions should match the appropriate picture. The fish sign is no longer 'secret' and on cars is now more a mark of distinction.	RE Non-statutory framework: Breadth of study (Religions and beliefs; Themes) QCA: Unit 5D How do the beliefs of Christians influence...?		Non-statutory AT2 Level 3/4
122	Where am I? Who am I?	To know where they live in relation to the European Community. To learn about the interdependence of communities.	Check the current EU membership before using this sheet. The map puzzle should be enlarged and mounted on card. Children will need access to a decent wall map of Europe or atlases.	PSHE and Citizenship NC guidelines: Preparing to play an active role as citizens QCA: Unit 7 Children's rights – human rights		N/A
123	My connections	To understand the interdependence of individuals, groups and communities.	Talk about the interconnected world. Children may be wearing trainers from China; their breakfast grapefruit may have come from South Africa and the music they listen to, from the USA.	PSHE and Citizenship NC guidelines: Developing good relationships... QCA: Unit 5 Living in a diverse world		N/A
124	People with power – your local authority	To have a simple understanding of democratic processes and institutions that support it locally and nationally.	For local services you might start with the refuse collectors. A local council website or a telephone directory will provide lists of departments and guides to the services they provide.	PSHE and Citizenship NC guidelines: Preparing to play an active role as citizens QCA: Unit 4 People who help us...		N/A
125	Feeling is understanding	To care about other people's feelings and to consider other people's needs.	Use adhesive dots (available from any stationers if your school does not have any) to raise the Braille dots above the surface of the paper.	PSHE and Citizenship NC guidelines: Developing good relationships... QCA: Unit 7 Children's rights – human rights		N/A
126	What is important?	To think about and recognise the importance of trust, honesty and respect.	Use the sheet as a focus for class discussion. Do any children notice that the titles to the cartoons are misnomers; they should be 'Distrust', 'Dishonesty' and 'Disrespect'.	PSHE and Citizenship NC guidelines: Developing good relationships... QCA: Unit 9 Respect for property		N/A
127	Tolerant people might...	To consider how and why we should demonstrate tolerance and respect for others.	Discussion should bring out the fact that tolerance is not an absolute and that being tolerant is not always easy.	PSHE and Citizenship NC guidelines: Developing good relationships... QCA: Unit 9 Respect for property		N/A

SCHOLASTIC
www.scholastic.co.uk

Letter strings

● Each word below contains a letter str**ing** (as in th**ing** and s**ing**le). There are four different letter strings in these words. Find them and underline them.

swimming	beard	bubbling	redundant
heard	ground	sound	currant
important	impound	earth	toasting

● Now write each string in the middle of a balloon, then add the words to the correct balloon strings!

● Put each word into a sentence to show its meaning.

Name _____

i before e?

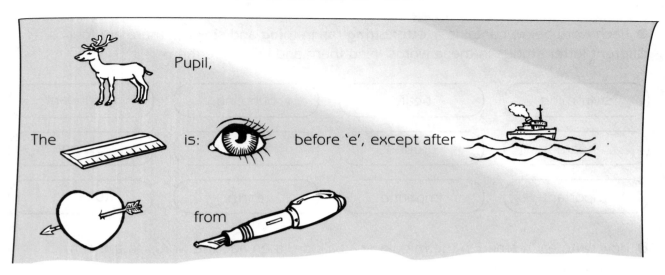

Pupil,

The [ruler] is: [eye] before 'e', except after [ship] .

from [pen]

● Learn the rule: **i** before **e** ⟶ except after **c**

br**ie**f _____ _____	rec**ei**ve _____ _____
th**ie**f _____ _____	conc**ei**t _____ _____
fr**ie**nd _____ _____	c**ei**ling _____ _____

BUT

These words do not follow the rule:

their	_____ _____ _____ _____
heir	_____ _____ _____ _____
weird	_____ _____ _____ _____

● Use dictionaries and spelling lists to add to each group of words. How many can you add?
● Choose three words from each group and write a sentence to show their meaning.

NO FUSS PHOTOCOPIABLE

Suffix towers

● Use the suffix at the base of each tower to build word towers as tall as you can. Can you find enough words to reach the top?

A **suffix** is a group of letters fixed to the end of a word and common to many words, for example **-ion**: perfection, selection, sensation, suspension.

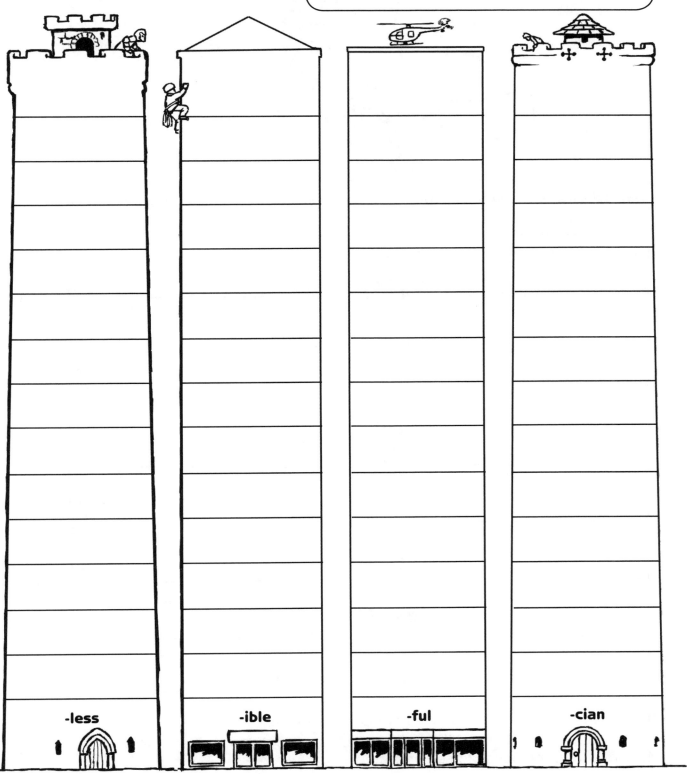

-less

-ible

-ful

-cian

● Check your words in a dictionary.

Name _____

Homophones

here hear

some sum

son sun

road rode

> **Homophones** are words that sound the same but are not spelled the same and have different meanings.

● Find the homophones. The pictures will help you.

pain	_____		plain	_____	
pair	_____		hair	_____	
sale	_____		stake	_____	
bury	_____		rows	_____	
thrown	_____		prints	_____	
break	_____		stalk	_____	
ate	_____		great	_____	

● Write out this sentence but use homophones to make it make sense.

My sun road to the beech to sea the sure.

More than one: plurals (1)

To make a word plural, for most words add **s**:

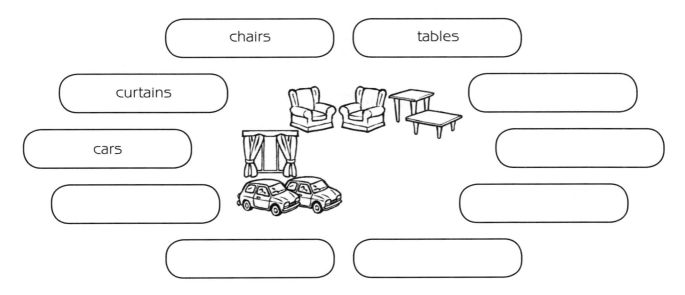

chairs	tables
curtains	
cars	

For most words ending in **s**, **sh** or **ch**, add **es**:

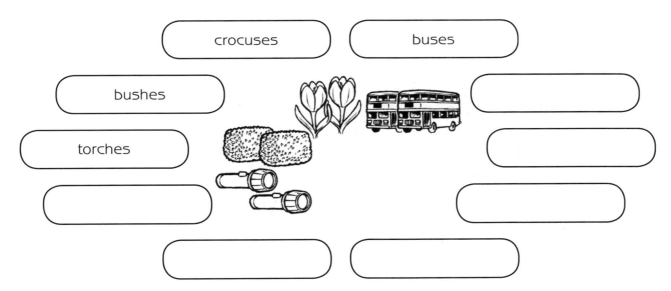

crocuses	buses
bushes	
torches	

Put these words in their correct group above by making them into plurals. Can you add any more? Use a dictionary to help you.

sink	marsh	stitch
flower	church	cat

NO FUSS
PHOTOCOPIABLE

CHAPTER 1

More than one: plurals (2)

Change **f** to **ves**:

thieves	knives	wives

When **y** is preceded by a consonant, change to **ies**:

babies   ponies

parties

jellies

When **y** is preceded by a vowel, add **s**:

toys   boys

keys

donkeys

Put these words in their correct group by making them into plurals. Can you add any more? Use a dictionary to help you.

curry	half	life	monkey
day	daisy	tray	hoof

NO FUSS
PHOTOCOPIABLE

SCHOLASTIC
www.scholastic.co.uk

Idiomatic phrases, clichés and expressions

● Match up the phrases with their meaning (write them out on a separate piece of paper). Use them in writing whenever you can.

Phrase	Meaning
smell a rat	in the same circumstances
throw in the towel	behave better
sit on the fence	give up
mind your ps and qs	have nothing to do
take forty winks	be like your father
out of sorts	avoid taking sides
hang your head	good enough
turn over a new leaf	suspect something
act the goat	misunderstand the situation
a chip of the old block	behave foolishly
at a loose end	be careful about the way you behave
play with fire	feel ashamed
keep the pot boiling	have a short sleep
in the same boat	risk serious trouble
up to the mark	not feeling yourself
taken for a ride	carry on with what you are doing
past his prime	be deliberately misled
barking up the wrong tree	no longer at his best

● Can you think of any other idioms or expressions?

Name _____

Prefixes

● Use a dictionary to find the meaning of these **prefixes**. Then find four words that begin with the prefix.

         meaning

in- _____not_____   inactive, inexpensive, inaccurate, insufficient _____

im- _____   _____

ir- _____   _____

il- _____   _____

pro- _____   _____

sus- _____   _____

● Take one word from each group and write it in a sentence to show its meaning.

_____

_____

_____

_____

_____

_____

● Do the same with these prefixes. Write your sentences on the back of the sheet.

auto- _____   _____

bi- _____   _____

trans- _____   _____

tele- _____   _____

micro- _____   _____

Onomatopoeia

Onomatopoeic words sound the same as the action or sound being described. For example, a horse **neighs**.

● Add to this collection of onomatopoeic words.

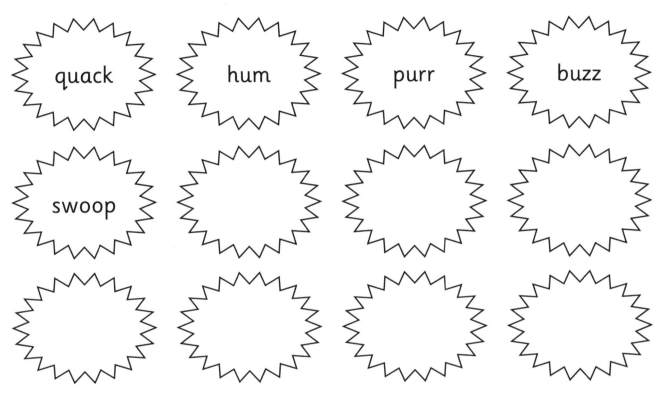

quack   hum   purr   buzz

swoop

● Invent some onomatopoeic words of your own.

● Use your onomatopoeic words in sentences.

_____

_____

_____

_____

Name _____

All change (1)

● Change these **verbs** to **nouns** by adding one of the **suffixes** from the wheels. Write the new word on the spoke of the correct wheel. One has been done for you.

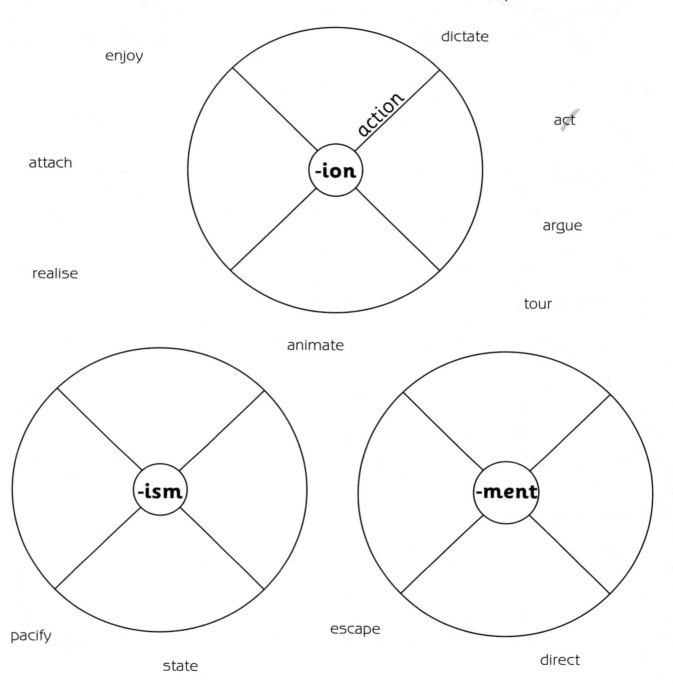

dictate

enjoy

act

attach

argue

realise

tour

animate

pacify

escape

state

direct

● Choose one word from each wheel and write a sentence to show its meaning.

_____

_____

_____

■SCHOLASTIC
www.scholastic.co.uk

All change (2)

● Change these **nouns** to **verbs** by adding one of the **suffixes** from the wheels. Write the new word on the spoke of the correct wheel.

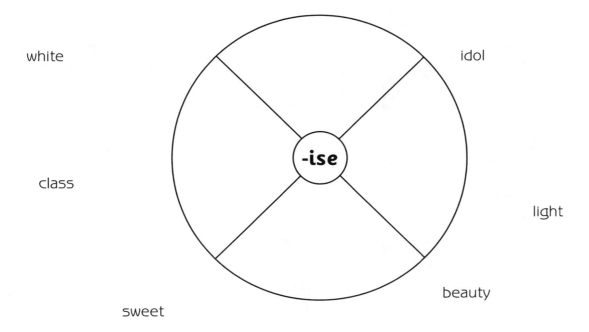

white

idol

class

light

beauty

sweet

-ise

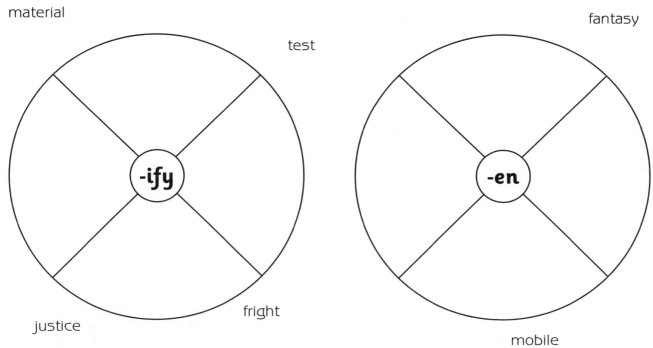

material

test

fantasy

justice

fright

mobile

-ify

-en

● Choose one word from each wheel and write a sentence to show its meaning.

Name _____

Auxiliary verbs

Grandma **was flying** to America.

auxiliary   main verb

Use a marker pen to highlight the **main verb** in each of these sentences. Can you see that there is another (auxiliary) verb in the sentence? Highlight the **auxiliary verbs** in a different colour. Study the example above before you begin.

1.   Perhaps we could bake a cake tonight?

2.   Fido has eaten too many Alabama mud pies.

3.   We will grow old one day.

4.   Margaret may come to your birthday party.

5.   They were all running towards us.

6.   Zimbabwe was called Rhodesia.

7.   The Post Office was named Consignia.

8.   I shall write a letter of complaint to the Mayor.

9.   They have built the tallest tower in the world.

10. We are going on a steam train.

SCHOLASTIC
www.scholastic.co.uk

From now to tomorrow

When we write about something that is to happen in the future we often need an extra (auxiliary) verb as well as the main verb to get the tense right. For example:

| I **shall fly** to Canada. | **fly** | main verb |
| | **shall** | auxiliary verb |

| They **will eat** fish on Friday. | **eat** | main verb |
| | **will** | auxiliary verb |

Change these verbs using an auxiliary verb so that the sentences describe something that will happen in the future.

1. Flo is a very good ballet dancer.

_____

2. Raji lives in Solihull.

_____

3. Arnold is on holiday in Cyprus.

_____

4. She is eating roast beef.

_____

5. Mona is enjoying her skiing lessons.

_____

6. Gandulf is a very fat dog.

_____

Name _____

From one person to another

	singular	plural
1st person	I	we
2nd person	you	you
3rd person	he, she, it	they

Use the chart above to work out which person the sentences below use. For example:
We are three little maids from school. (1st person plural)

sentence	person
When will they ever learn?	
Baa baa Black Sheep, have you any wool?	
They charged into the Valley of Death.	
Nasser scored 100 runs against India.	
Do you all sing in the choir?	
I am going to bed now.	

■ SCHOLASTIC
www.scholastic.co.uk

Direct speech

To write direct speech you must use inverted commas and the words actually spoken. For example: "Let me try on the glass slipper," said the Ugly Sister.

Use direct speech to complete these sentences correctly. The first one is done for you.

"Ding, dong!" chimed the clock. _____

The Prince shouted, _____

_____ moaned the footman.

_____ twittered the bird.

_____ asked the coach.

Cinderella said, _____

Name _____

Direct speech – reported speech

To write reported speech you do **not** use inverted commas or all of the words actually spoken. For example:

D   "Will you try on the glass slipper, Cinderella?" asked the Prince.

> **R**   The Prince asked Cinderella to try on the glass slipper.

Try writing reported speech for yourself.

D   "Shall I clean and cook or marry a prince?" wondered Cinderella.

> **R**

D   "Leave our pumpkins alone!" shouted the Ugly Sisters at the Fairy Godmother.

> **R**

D   "Shall I turn the Ugly Sisters into toads?" asked the Fairy Godmother.

> **R**

D   The footman moaned, "I haven't got a fairy godmother."

> **R**

SCHOLASTIC
www.scholastic.co.uk

Directions for dialogue

When we write down **dialogue** (speech involving more than one person), we need to keep certain rules.

●   Use speech marks around the words actually spoken.
●   Start a new line when a different person speaks.

For example: "Can you see England yet?" asked Pete the pilot.
                 "It's too cloudy to tell," replied Benji the navigator.

Write out this conversation keeping to the rules.

Judging by the instruments, Pete the pilot remarked, we don't have much fuel left. You always worry too much replied Benji the navigator sitting behind him. According to my calculations we are only 200 miles from base. I am sure we can make it. But the pilot continued to worry and did not remain silent for long. I think we ought to make for Brize Norton airfield Pete said after a few minutes. Oh no Benji exclaimed. Brize Norton is a long way from my home and I left my Ferrari in the car park at Gatwick. If we run out of fuel you won't even be driving a roller skate responded Pete angrily. You could let me jump out joked Benji. My mum would love to see me arrive home by parachute. I'll throw you out if you aren't quiet threatened Pete.

NO FUSS
PHOTOCOPIABLE

Name _____

Writing a script

> **Playwrights** write **playscripts**. A playscript:
> – shows who says what
> – includes production notes for the producer.

Turn this story into a play. Write who says what and provide stage directions. It has been started for you.

Script	Production notes
Police officer: Ullo, ullo! What's going on here?	Broken bike on floor
Zoe:	

Writing for radio

Write a short playscript for a radio programme. You must use the props, characters and setting shown below. (You can add extra if you wish.) Plan your plot first. Write out the dialogue and include production notes.

Props

Setting

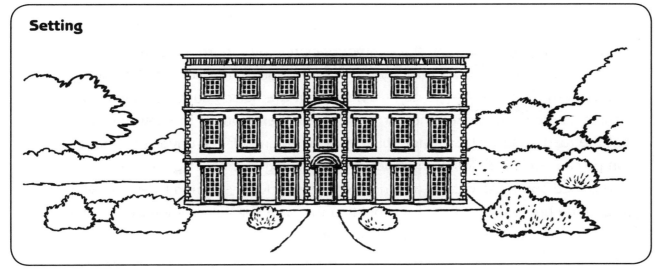

Characters

| Molly the Maid | Lord Arthur | Lady Arthur | Chief Inspector Noble | Roger the Robber |

NO FUSS PHOTOCOPIABLE

YEAR 5 AGES 9-10   33

Name _____

Points of view

Because there had been quite a lot of accidents in Beechcroft Road, the council erected some speed bumps. Not everyone approved of them. One man crashed his car into a tree the day after they were built because he swerved after failing to see them. Some residents complained about the noise caused by vehicles braking as they approached the bumps. One mother wrote to the newspaper to say that the road was much safer for children now. An ambulance driver said that the bumps caused him to lose time when he was racing to an emergency. Someone complained about the cost of making them. Fast drivers seemed to enjoy swerving around the bumps as fast as they could. In the six weeks since they were installed no pedestrian has been hurt in a road accident.

Are speed bumps good or bad?
Decide what your point of view is and list your arguments as bullet points:

●

●

●

Persuasive devices

● When people want to win an argument they sometimes use all sorts of persuasive tricks and devices. Have you heard or read these phrases?

> **1.** Clearly the truth is…
>
> **2.** Only a fool would believe…
>
> **3.** Every right-thinking person…

● Can you explain what these phrases are trying to do?

1. _____

_____

2. _____

_____

3. _____

_____

● Find some more examples. Collect phrases from your reading, from advertisements and so on.

Name _____

Getting it wrong

Newspaper headlines, notices and labels often shorten sentences to save space. This can make their meaning ambiguous. Look at these examples.

● llustrate these showing that you have got the meaning wrong.

Police arrest man with golf club

Parking for mother and child

Holidays in the sun!

Smith thrashes the champion!

NO FUSS PHOTOCOPIABLE

■ **SCHOLASTIC**
www.scholastic.co.uk

A pile of prepositions

The **bone** is (under) the **chair**.

preposition

The preposition **under** shows how the nouns **bone** and **chair** relate to each other.

Here is another example:

They **jumped** (across) the **puddle**.

They and **puddle** are related by the preposition **across**.

Highlight the **prepositions** in these sentences.

1. It rained, and the **water** dripped off her **nose**.

2. She put her **head** in her **hands** and cried.

3. The **osprey** dived towards the **sea**.

4. **They** tripped over the **dog**.

5. The **chickens** ran down the **road**.

6. A few exhausted **firefighters** were resting against the **wall**.

7. "Put the **key** through the **letterbox**!" shouted the woman.

8. Without stopping, **he** drove to **Truro**.

9. She kept the **money** behind the **cornflakes packet**.

(by)   (down)

(for)   (back)

(to)   (behind)

(with)   (through)

(around)   (off)

(against)   (up)

(over)   (on)

(from)   (in)

(towards)

Name _____

I protest!

The Planning Officer
Barsetshire County Council
County Hall Buildings
Rumsey Road
Barset
BT1 4PN

The Headteacher
Sunshine Primary School
Meadow Flower Lane
Cuddlecombe
Barsetshire
BT27 5XG

20th July 2003

Dear Headteacher

This letter is to inform you that the council is building a
refuse disposal facility at the end of your school's
playing field. It will be state of the art, so noise and
smell will be kept to a minimum. Between 4 and 15 lorries
an hour will deliver to the site at peak times but there
will be no deliveries on Sunday (although the bulldozer
will operate then). The council will doubleglaze your
offices to keep out the noise and put a high wire fence
around the playground to catch the rubbish blown by the
wind.

Unfortunately we will need to use part of your football
pitch for the access road but we will compensate you
financially.

I am sure that you will welcome this facility as it will
benefit the residents of the village because it is cheaper
to dump their rubbish here than in the quarry at Moorend.

Yours faithfully

N. O. Brain

N. O. Brain
Planning Officer

Taking temperatures

1. Take these temperatures.

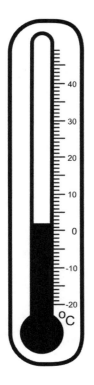  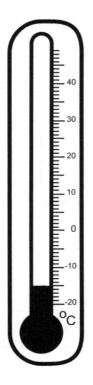 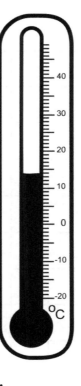 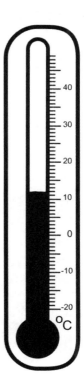

a. _____ b. _____ c. _____ d. _____ e. _____

2. Arrange the temperatures in order, lowest first.

_____°C _____°C _____°C _____°C _____°C

3. What is the difference in temperature between the highest and
lowest temperatures? _____

4. How many degrees does the temperature fall from 2°C to –6°C? _____

5. How much must the temperature rise by from –12°C to –6°C? _____

6. When the temperature rises by 16°C, show what this thermometer
will look like.

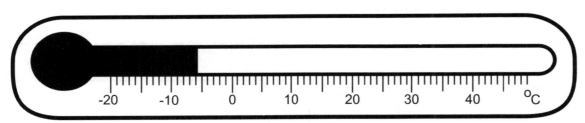

NO
FUSS
PHOTOCOPIABLE

Name _____

All square

● Use coloured pencils to build up squares 1 × 1, 2 × 2, 3 × 3, and so on, on this grid. Complete up to 10 × 10. Fill in the table below too.

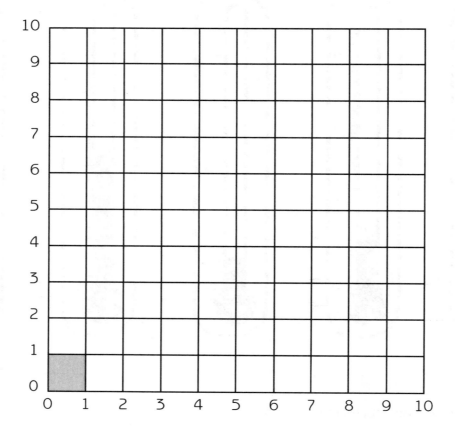

1 × 1 = 1² =1
2 × 2 =
3
4
5
6
7
8
9
10

● What is 9²? _____

● What is the area of a square swimming pool 9 metres long? _____

● What is five squared? _____

● Explain in your own words what a square number is.

_____

_____

_____

_____

NO FUSS
PHOTOCOPIABLE

■SCHOLASTIC
www.scholastic.co.uk

For every...

1. For every goal that Kafu scores, Rinaldo scores two. Kafu scored 31 goals in the season. How many did Rinaldo score?

_____

In one match Rinaldo scored 4 goals. How many did Kafu score?

_____

2. Javed eats five sweets for every two that Natasha eats. Javed eats 25 sweets. How many does Natasha eat?

_____

3. For every leg a bird has, a spider has 4. How many legs does a spider have?

_____

4. For every 5 books that Philip reads, Rosie reads 10. Rosie reads 30 books. How many did Philip read?

_____

5. Gran uses 3 apples to make ¼ litre of sauce. How many apples are needed to make 2 litres?

_____

NO
FUSS
PHOTOCOPIABLE

YEAR 5 AGES 9-10   **41**

Name _____

Decimals, fractions and percentages

● Complete this chart. Then learn these facts.

fraction	decimal	%
1	1.00	
$\frac{1}{2}$		50%
		75%
$\frac{1}{4}$		
$\frac{1}{5}$		
	0.10	
$\frac{1}{100}$		

● What percentage of these shapes is shaded?

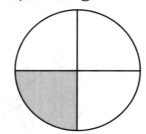

a. _____

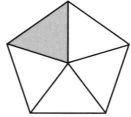

b. _____

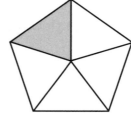

c. _____

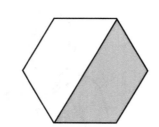

d. _____

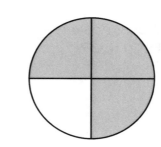

e. _____

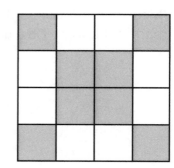

f. _____

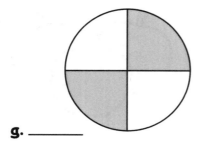

g. _____

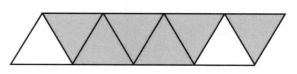

h. _____

Leftovers

When you divide one number by another it does not always go exactly. What can we do about the leftovers? We can use fractions in our answers:

$$32 \div 9 = 3\tfrac{5}{9}$$

● Write these quotients using fractions. The first has been done for you.

a. $33 \div 8 = 4\tfrac{1}{8}$ **e.** $18 \div 7 =$

b. $35 \div 6 =$ **f.** $27 \div 4 =$

c. $49 \div 5 =$ **g.** $39 \div 8 =$

d. $73 \div 6 =$ **h.** $61 \div 5 =$

● Sometimes it is not sensible to use fractions in your answers. Calculate your answers to the questions below. Will you need to use fractions?

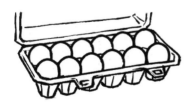

1. An egg box holds 12 eggs. There are 74 eggs. How many boxes are needed?

2. A school takes 120 children on a trip to the zoo. Each coach holds 35 children. How many coaches are needed?

3. Opera tickets cost £48 each. How many can I buy for £250?

Name _____

Estimate and calculate

Look at each calculation. Which of the three answers given do you think is correct? Circle that answer in red then use a calculator to work out the correct answer. Underline it. If your guess was correct score a point. How many points do you score out of 21?

1.	5 × 555 =	3421	2775	2510
2.	8 × 324 =	2592	4341	2012
3.	9 × 998 =	8982	8132	9832
4.	512 ÷ 8 =	50	64	36
5.	405 ÷ 9 =	68	54	45
6.	400 ÷ 16 =	20	25	31
7.	18 × 21 =	378	278	478
8.	28 × 31 =	758	998	868
9.	38 × 41 =	1738	1248	1558
10.	1296 ÷ 36 =	36	26	16
11.	576 ÷ 24 =	14	24	34
12.	289 ÷ 17 =	17	10	27
13.	72 × 55 =	3960	3510	3110
14.	44 × 71 =	2814	3124	3334
15.	85 × 34 =	890	1890	2890
16.	600 ÷ 25 =	23	24	21
17.	1024 ÷ 16 =	64	60	75
18.	1426 ÷ 23 =	62	32	82
19.	91 × 91 =	6171	8281	9111
20.	39 × 82 =	2998	3599	3198
21.	55 × 93 =	5115	6115	4995

NO FUSS
PHOTOCOPIABLE

Hot shot!

Shoot down the numbers one at a time using your calculator keys. You must shoot them in size order starting with the smallest number. Record your key presses as shown below.

	key presses	display
	⊟ 2 ⊜	5470
	⊟ 7 0 ⊜	5400
	⊟ 4 0 0 ⊜	5000
	⊟ 5 0 0 0 ⊜	0

a. 7635

b. 1996

c. 4082

d. 9301

e. 3670

f. 9999

g. 10132

h. 25461

i. 43195

j. 72346

Polyominoes

Polyominoes are made from identical squares touching fully edge to edge.

There is only one monomino.

There is only one domino.

But you can make two trominoes. (If you make others you will find that they are the same as these but rotated or turned over.)

There are five tetrominoes.

● Here is one pentomino, but there are many more. Can you find them all?

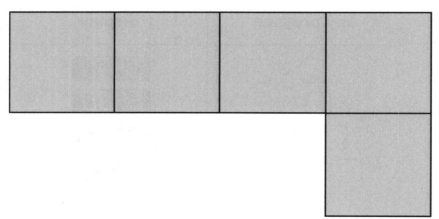

● Complete the chart:

Polyomino chart		
name	number of squares	number of possible arrangements
monomino	I	I
domino	2	
tromino		
tetromino		
pentomino		

NO FUSS PHOTOCOPIABLE

It's a problem (1)

1. To cook the chicken the oven was set to come on at 4.45pm and to go off at 6.20pm. For how long was the chicken cooked?

_____

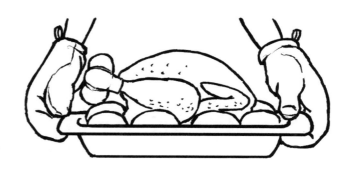

2. The video player started recording at 21.15 and stopped at 23.35. For how long did it record?

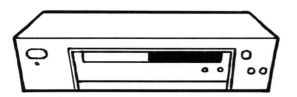

_____

3. It was 325 miles to Rye. The coach had travelled 112 miles. How much further to go?

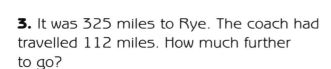

_____

4. Mum's car does 42 miles to the gallon. She has used 9 gallons of petrol since Friday. How far has she travelled?

_____

Name _____

It's a problem (2)

1. There are 21 bags of sugar in a large cardboard box. Each bag contains 2.2kg of sugar. Someone drops the box bursting 5 bags. How many kilograms of sugar are left that can be sold undamaged?

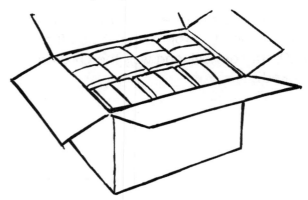

_____

2. The bank will exchange 1 Euro for every 65p. How much money will I need to exchange for 20 Euros?

_____

3. In a grand sale there is 20% off everything except lampshades and lamps which both have 50% off. How much would you save on the price of each of these items in the sale?

£1020   £86.50   £320   £24   £133   £180

a._____ b._____ c._____ d._____ e._____ f._____

4. 80 people from the village want to go to the Flower Show at the NEC. They decide to go by sharing cars. They have 20 cars between them and although they can each carry 5 people, 75% of the cars are fitted with seatbelts for 4 people only. Can they all go to the Flower Show in one journey without breaking the law?

_____

NO FUSS
PHOTOCOPIABLE

■SCHOLASTIC
www.scholastic.co.uk

Know your measures

● Complete and remember:

A **mile** is a bit more than 1.5 kilometres and is a measure of _____.

A **gallon** is a bit less than 5 litres and is a measure of _____.

A **pint** is slightly more than 0.5 litres and is a measure of _____.

● Match the measures as shown.

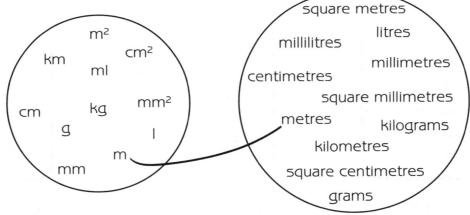

● Complete:

1. 474cm = _____ m

2. 3251cm = _____ m

3. 1400ml = _____ l

4. 5500ml = _____ l

5. 4300g = _____ kg

6. 6500g = _____ kg

Name _____

Using the right measure

● Fill in suitable units of measurement.

I measured my
fish in…

I measured the length
of the classroom in…

I weighed my
fish in…

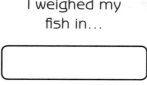

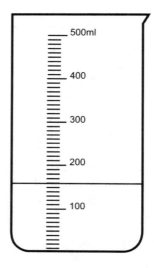

I measured the area
of the field in…

● Pour on water…

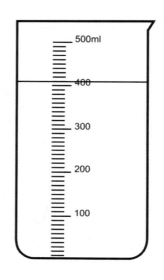

| 500ml |
| 400 |
| 300 |
| 200 |
| 100 |

a. add 200ml

b. add 50ml

c. add 360ml

● Measure these lines to the nearest mm.

d. _____

e. _____

f. _____

NO FUSS PHOTOCOPIABLE

■ SCHOLASTIC
www.scholastic.co.uk

Name _____

Calculating areas

● These shapes are built from m². What are their areas?

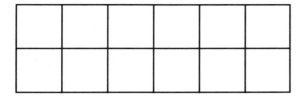

a. _____

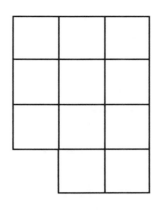

b. _____

c. _____

● Calculate the areas of these rectangles.

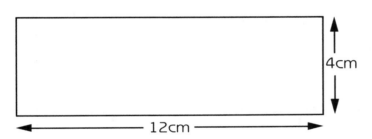

4cm

12cm

d. _____

5cm

5cm

e. _____

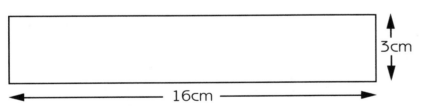

3cm

16cm

f. _____

11cm

12cm

g. _____

● What is the **approximate** area of these rectangles?

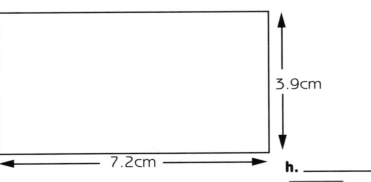

3.9cm

7.2cm

h. _____

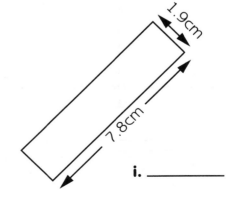

1.9cm

7.8cm

i. _____

Name _____

Area and perimeter

● Calculate the area of each shape in cm² as accurately as you can.
● Measure the perimeter of each shape to the nearest mm.

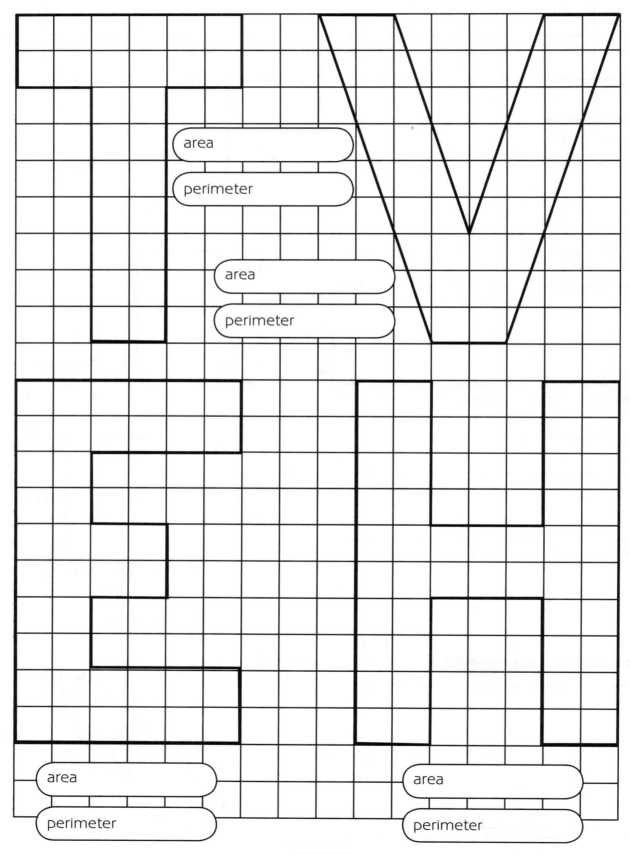

area

perimeter

area

perimeter

area

perimeter

area

perimeter

PHOTOCOPIABLE

The right time

● Stick these pictures in the correct places.

● Look at this timetable and answer the questions below.

Timetable					
Oxford	Didcot Parkway	Reading	Slough	Ealing Broadway	London Paddington
05.33	05.54 c	06.12	06.20	. . .	06.40
06.40	06.58	07.20	. . .	. . .	07.39
08.22	08.44 c	09.05	09.15	. . .	09.30
08.46	09.00	09.18	. . .	. . .	09.44
08.57	. . .	. . .	. . .	. . .	09.47
09.15 sx	. . .	09.51	. . .	. . .	10.11
09.58	. . .	10.38	. . .	. . .	10.52
10.27	10.45 c	11.05	11.18	11.26	11.36

c   Change at Didcot Parkway

sx   Saturdays excepted

1. How long does it take for the 08.46 from Oxford to reach Reading?   _____

2. Which is the fastest train to Slough from Oxford?   _____

3. Which is the slowest train from Oxford to Paddington?   _____

4. How many trains run after 09.00 from Reading on a Saturday?   _____

5. Can I get a train from Oxford to Slough without changing?   _____

NO FUSS
PHOTOCOPIABLE

Name _____

Missing links

Link the descriptions to the shapes by drawing a connecting line where they match.

a polygon with three sides and three angles – all angles and sides are equal
a regular six-sided polygon
a polygon with eight equal sides and angles
an irregular polygon with seven sides
a polygon with four sides
a triangle with two equal sides and two equal angles
a triangle with all angles and sides unequal
a five-sided irregular polygon

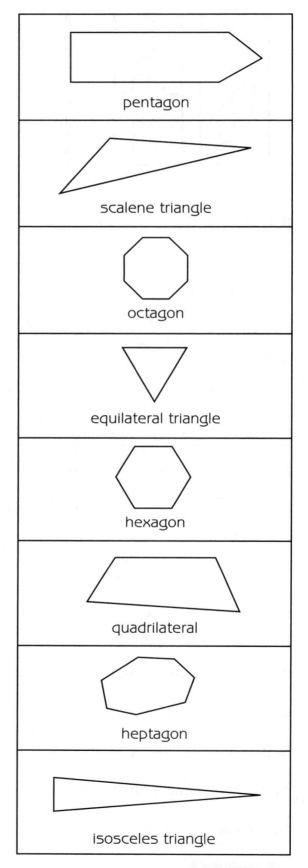

pentagon

scalene triangle

octagon

equilateral triangle

hexagon

quadrilateral

heptagon

isosceles triangle

NO FUSS
PHOTOCOPIABLE

Name _____

Making reflections

● Complete these reflections in the mirror line.

1.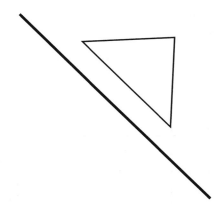

2.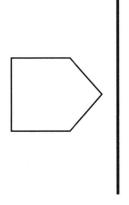

3.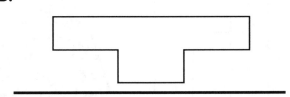

4.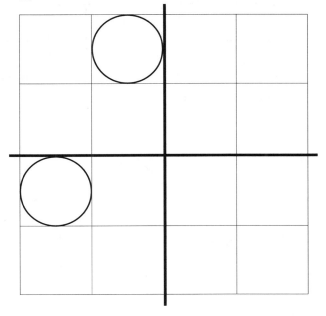

● These reflections have **two** axes of symmetry. Complete the patterns.

5.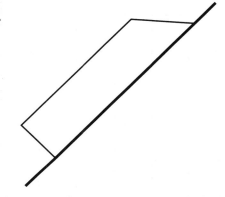

6.

Name _____

Coordinated shapes

● Label the x-axis and the y-axis on the grid below.
● Mark the coordinates (1,4) (7,8) (1,8) and (7,4) in **red**.
They form the vertices of a shape. Draw the shape. What is it? _____
● Mark the coordinates (4,2) (8,10) (0,10) in **blue**.
They form the vertices of a shape. Draw the shape. What is it? _____

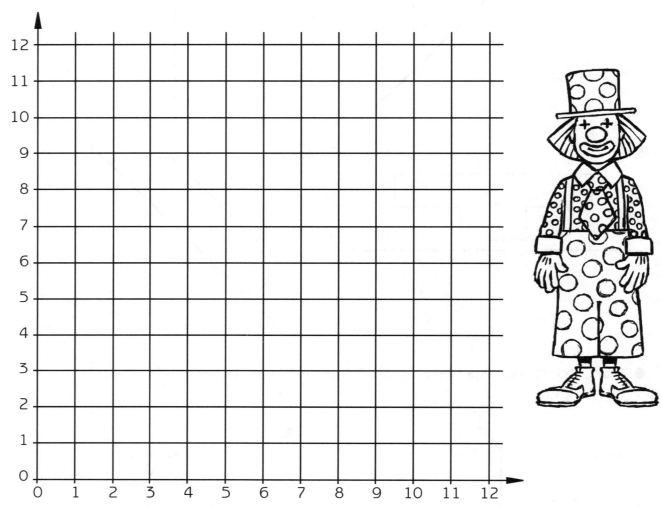

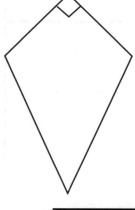

● In the shapes below, draw over the **parallel** lines in **red** and the **perpendicular** lines in **green**. Use a ruler to draw accurately.

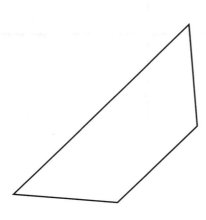

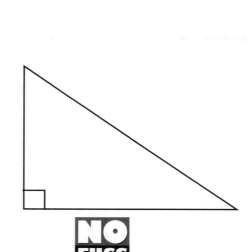

NO FUSS
PHOTOCOPIABLE

■ SCHOLASTIC
www.scholastic.co.uk

Measurement by degrees

● You will need a protractor to measure these angles.

1. _____

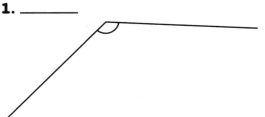

2. _____

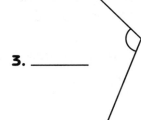

3. _____

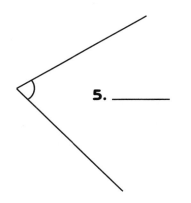

4. _____

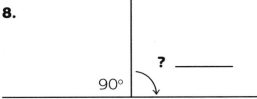

5. _____

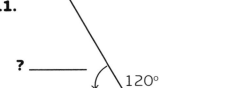

● **Calculate** the missing angles.

6.

? _____   35°

7.

? _____   76°

8.

90°   ? _____

9.

45°   ? _____

10.

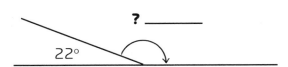

? _____   22°

11.

? _____   120°

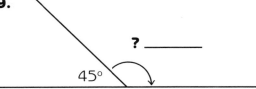

Name _____

Know your angles

Learn and remember that:
● the angle of a **straight line** is 180°
● an angle between 90° and 180° is **obtuse**
● an angle less than 90° is **acute**
● an angle of 90° is a **right angle**.

Being obtuse…

Cut out these balloons and stick the angles in the correct chart.

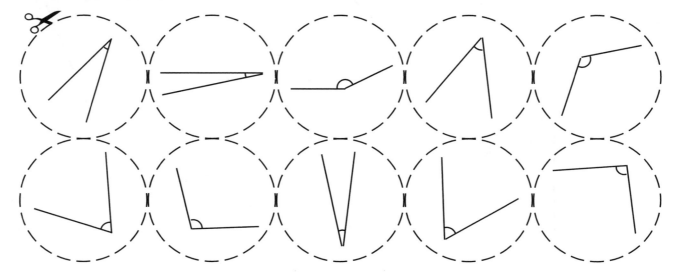

acute angles	obtuse angles

NO FUSS
PHOTOCOPIABLE

■ SCHOLASTIC
www.scholastic.co.uk

Accident and Emergency graph

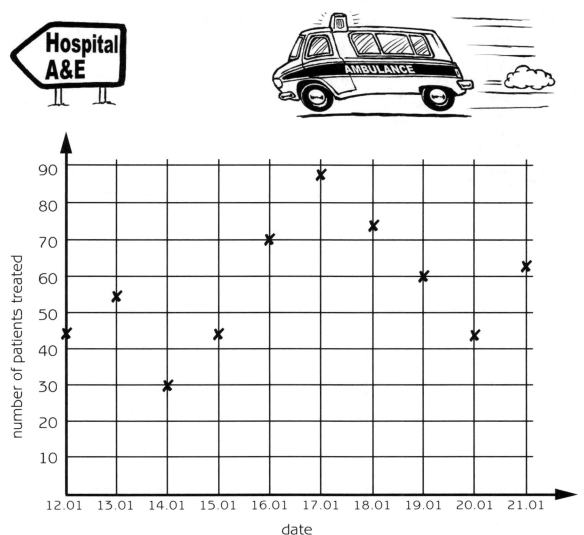

1. What is the total number of patients treated between 12.01 and 21.01 inclusive? _____

2. What was the most common number of patients treated (the mode)? _____

3. What was the greatest number of patients treated in any one day? _____

4. On how many days were fewer than 40 patients treated? _____

5. Can you think of possible reasons why nearly three times as many patients were treated on the 17.01 than on the 14.01?

_____

_____

_____

Name _____

Milkman's maths: line graph

At the Meldrew Retirement Home the residents love to drink tea –
lots of it. Here are the milk deliveries for one week in October.

DAY	Mon	Tue	Wed	Thur	Fri	Sat	Sun
Bottles delivered	18	13	16	16	9	20	6

● Plot the line graph of these deliveries.

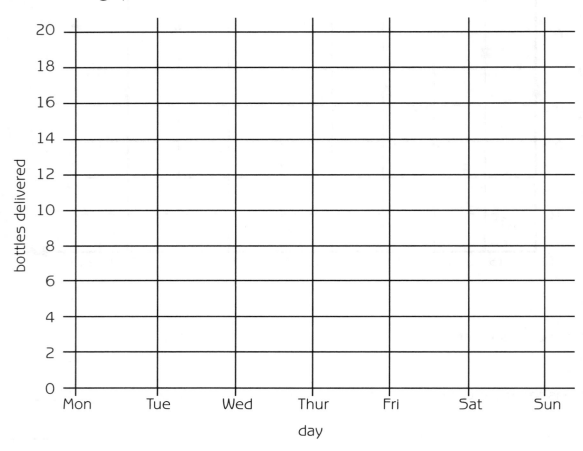

● From the data work out:

• the mode _____   • the range _____

● Can you suggest any reasons why Sunday's delivery was the smallest?

_____

_____

_____

Healthy connections

The food we eat every day is called our **diet**. **Health** and **diet** are connected but people did not always know this.

● Use books to find out about food and vitamins then see if you can make the right connections below.

What was the problem?	**What did they do about it?**

Scurvy
Sailors on long voyages became ill with scurvy due to a lack of vitamin C.

Fed them potatoes, lemon juice and milk.

Rickets
Young children developed soft bones that became bent due to a lack of vitamin D.

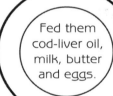
Fed them cod-liver oil, milk, butter and eggs.

The death of babies
In Paris, babies from rich families had a diet containing less vitamin C than the babies from poor families so more rich babies died.

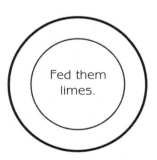
Fed them limes.

Brain teaser
● Why did the Americans give the British the nickname 'Limeys'?

_____

_____

Name _____

Trace a torso: the heart and lungs

● Trace each rectangle and the drawings they contain onto tracing paper. Cut the rectangles out. Put the body together correctly by placing the sheets on top of each other.

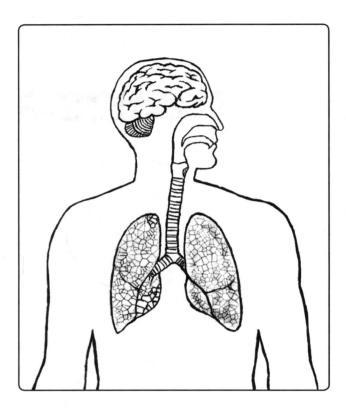

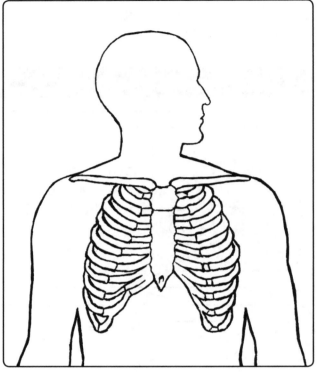

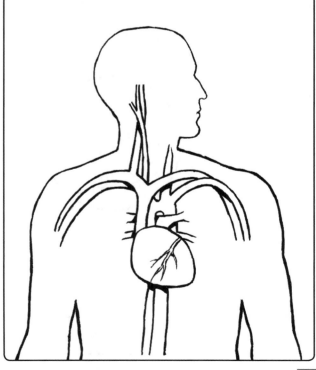

● Find out:

● What protects the heart and lungs?

_____

● Why does the muscle in the wall of the heart contract regularly?

_____

● Add to the drawings. Label the brain, lungs and any organ you can name to which the heart pumps blood.

NO FUSS
PHOTOCOPIABLE

Name _____

Seed dispersal

● Seeds can be dispersed in a variety of ways. How are these seeds dispersed? Put them in the correct column in the table below.

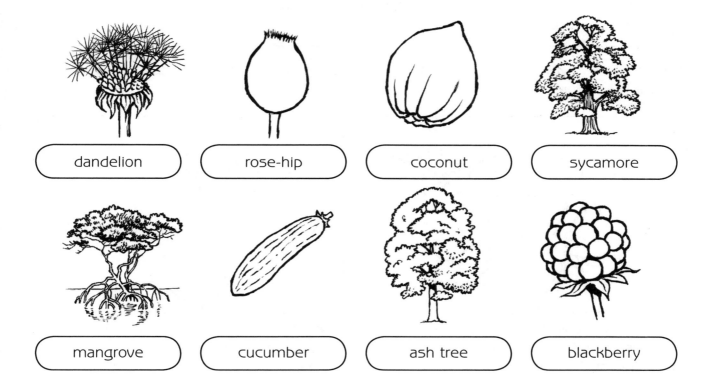

| dandelion | rose-hip | coconut | sycamore |

| mangrove | cucumber | ash tree | blackberry |

water	wind	explosion	animal

● Why might some seeds not grow into new plants?

_____

● Why do plants produce so many seeds?

_____

Name _____

Pollination

Most flowers have **male** and **female** parts. The **stamens** are a flower's male parts and produce **pollen**. The **stigma** and the **ovary** are the female parts. Pollen settles on the stigma and **fertilises** the seeds. Seeds will not grow unless they have been fertilised.

● Study the pictures and read the text. Colour pollen yellow and show its journey from picture to picture.

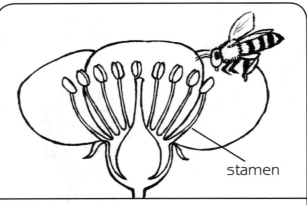

stamen

1. When collecting nectar an insect brushes against the stamens and pollen sticks to its legs and body.

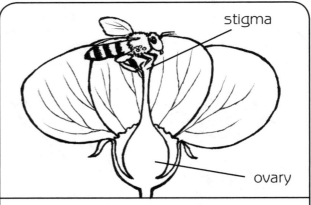

stigma

ovary

2. When the insect visits another flower, pollen brushes from its body against the stigma.

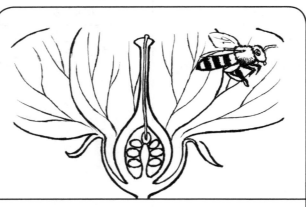

3. The pollen passes down the stigma to the ovum where it fertilises the seeds.

4. When the seeds are ripe they disperse. If they land on moist, light ground, a new plant will grow.

● Not all flowers are pollinated by insects: pollen can also be carried by animals such as birds and bats. Find two other ways in which flowers can be pollinated.

_____

_____

NO FUSS PHOTOCOPIABLE

Guess the gas

● Air has weight and is all around us, but you can't see it. How do you know that it exists?
● There are many gases. Can you name the gases used in the pictures below?

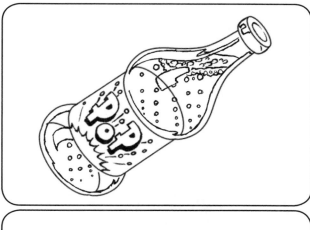

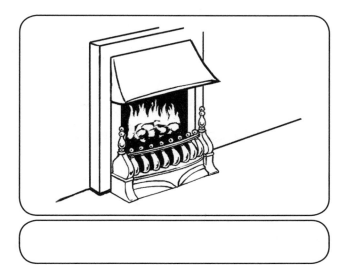

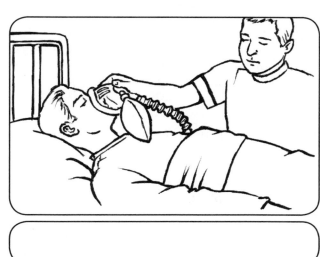

● Draw two other examples showing where gases are important to us.

CHAPTER 3

Solids, liquids and gases

● Do the activities drawn below with a friend. Talk about what is happening.

Pour water from
bottle to glass.

Push in a syringe filled with
air, then water, then sand.

Fill a balloon with
air, then water.

Transfer flour from
container to bowl.

Release the stopper
on a bottle of perfume.

Take the lid off a
fizzy drink bottle.

● Think about the differences between solids, liquids and gases and then write down as many differences as you can think of on the chart below.

solids	liquids	gases
have a definite shape	take on the shape of their containers	

NO FUSS PHOTOCOPIABLE

■ SCHOLASTIC
www.scholastic.co.uk

Changing state: evaporation

● What happens to puddles when it stops raining?

● What happens to wet washing when it is hung on the washing line?

_____

_____

_____

_____

● What happens to…?

● What happens to…?

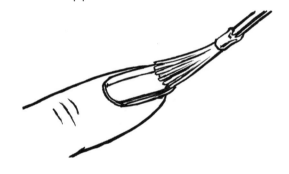

_____

_____

_____

_____

Evaporation is when a liquid turns to gas.

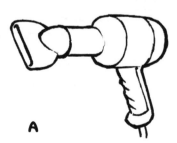

A

B

C

● Explain how these (**A**, **B** and **C**) help to dry things more quickly.

A _____

B _____

C _____

Name _____

Changing state: condensation

Condensation is when a gas turns to a liquid. It is the **reverse** of evaporation.

● What happens to water vapour when it cools down?

_____

_____

● On which surfaces will water vapour condense in these rooms? Mark them.

● Complete the sentence:

Air contains w_____ v_____. When this hits a c _____ surface,

it forms c _____.

● Why is there less condensation on windows on a warm day?

_____

Name _____

The water cycle

● Cut out the labels and stick them in the correct places on the picture to show what happens in the water cycle.

| water vapour condenses | water evaporates | sea | rain | river | moving air/wind |

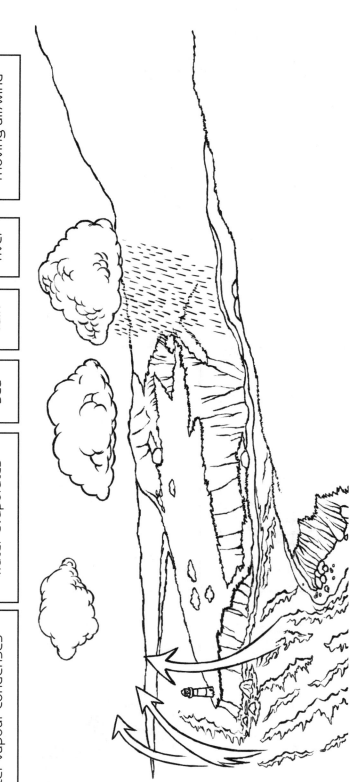

● Fill in the gaps:

Water _____ from oceans and lakes. Water vapour _____ as clouds and eventually falls as _____. Water collects in streams and _____ and eventually finds its way back to the _____.

● Where does your drinking water comes from?

Name _____

Heavens above!

● The Sun, Moon and Earth are approximately spherical. Think about how big they are. Which of these spheres would you choose to represent each heavenly body?

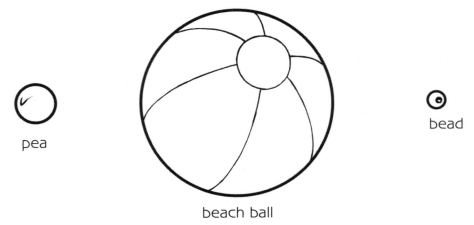

pea

beach ball

bead

_____   _____   _____

The Sun does not move.

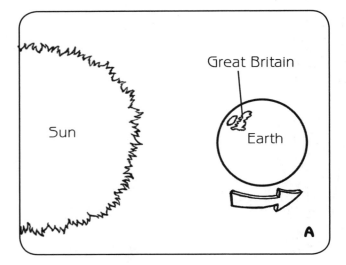

Great Britain

Sun

Earth

A

The Earth spins on its axis.

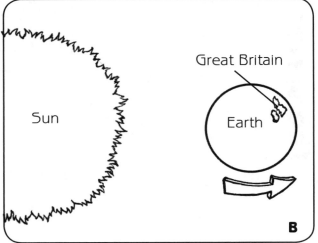

Great Britain

Sun

Earth

B

● With a friend, use a torch (to represent the Sun) and a globe in a dark corner of a room to help you decide in which picture **A** or **B** (above) you would be asleep in bed. Explain your answer.

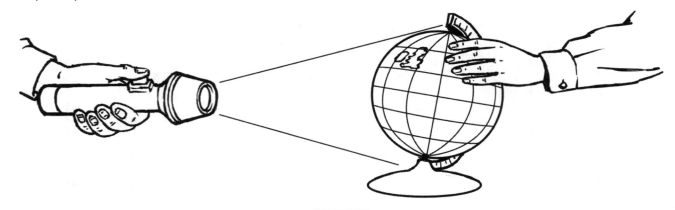

The Moon's orbit

The Moon appears to change shape because of the way the Sun shines on it as it circles the Earth.
The Moon orbits the Earth roughly once a month.

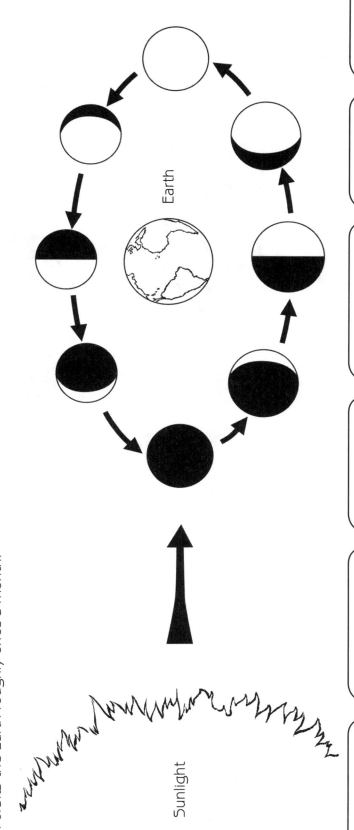

Earth

Sunlight

Half of the moon is lit up when it is a quarter of the way round its orbit.

It is a **new Moon** when the Moon is between us and the Sun.

As the Moon moves around the Earth, some sunlight catches the edge of the Moon and we see a **crescent Moon**.

When the Moon is exactly opposite the Sun, all the sunlight falls on its surface and it is a **full Moon**.

More and more of the Moon is lit up as it orbits the Earth. It reaches its **gibbous** stage when a crescent appears to have been cut out of it.

The changes are reversed as the Moon continues to orbit the Earth – from **gibbous** to **half Moon** to **crescent Moon** and finally, to **new Moon** again.

Draw an arrow from each label to the correct phase of the Moon.

Name _____

Vibrations

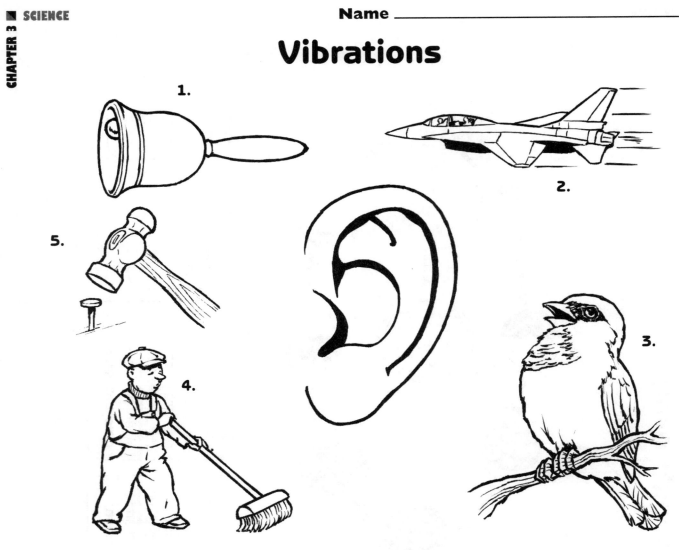

What sound is being made in each picture? Describe it. Is it high-pitched or low-pitched? How do you think that the sound is being made? What is vibrating?

1. _____

_____

2. _____

_____

3. _____

_____

4. _____

_____

5. _____

_____

NO FUSS
PHOTOCOPIABLE

SCHOLASTIC
www.scholastic.co.uk

Metronome muffling

> **You will need:** a metronome, a cardboard box large enough to put it in, bubble wrap, carpet, and a selection of other fabrics.

● Set the metronome and put it in the empty box. Shut the lid. What happens to the sound?

_____

Experiment

● Use different materials to line the box and make a fair test to see which are best at muffling the sound. Record your results for each material. Predict what might happen first.

Material	Prediction	What actually happens

Name _____

Changing pitch: wind instruments

Pitch is how high or low a sound is.

In wind instruments, the pitch changes according to the length of the column of air that is vibrated. The bigger the column, the lower the pitch.

● Place these instruments in order, according to pitch, starting with the lowest-pitched instrument.

Answer: _____

_____

Pan pipes – make and test
● Play the pipes by blowing across the top of each tube. Which tubes make the highest notes? Can you explain why?

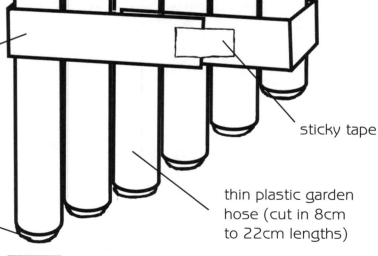

stiff card

sticky tape

bunged-up ends (Plasticine®, cork or tape)

thin plastic garden hose (cut in 8cm to 22cm lengths)

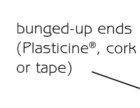
NO FUSS PHOTOCOPIABLE

Changing pitch: stringed instruments

● Tie a piece of string (80cm) to a chair leg. Pull it tight. Twang it. Try this several times using a different length, thickness and tightness of string. Describe what happens to the pitch of the notes that you make.

_____

_____

_____

_____

_____

The violin family
● Match the labels to the correct instrument.

(cello) (violin) (viola) (double bass)

● Which has the lowest pitch. Why?

_____

Name _____

Banging on

● What do you think will affect the pitch of a drum? Write your prediction here.

_____

_____

_____

● Now bang a drum!

Use a drum whose skin can be tightened by turning these screws.

● Finish the sentences:

When I tightened the screws, I found that _____

_____

_____

When I loosened the screws, I found that _____

_____

_____

● Put these drums in order of pitch, starting with the lowest-pitched drum.

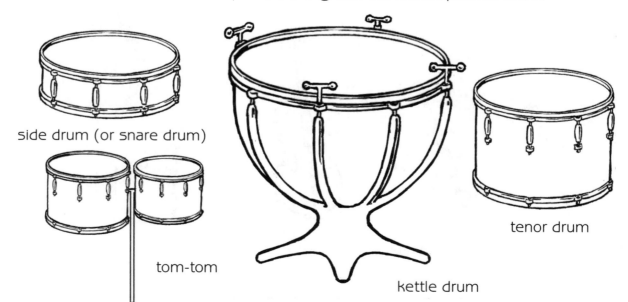

side drum (or snare drum)

tom-tom

kettle drum

tenor drum

NO FUSS
PHOTOCOPIABLE

SCHOLASTIC
www.scholastic.co.uk

Images of a queen: Victoria

● Here are three pictures of Queen Victoria. Which pieces of text do they go with? Cut out the pictures and text and arrange them in chronological order (where you can) to make an illustrated article about the Victorian age.

Queen Victoria reigned for almost 64 years. This is longer than any other British monarch. She died in 1901 aged 81.

Victoria married Prince Albert and had nine children. When Albert died in 1861 at the age of 42, she went into mourning and never fully recovered. She withdrew from public life for many years. She left all Albert's rooms just as they were when he died.

When she was only 18 years old in 1837, Victoria's uncle, King William IV, died. She became Queen.

During Victoria's long reign Britain changed enormously. When she came to the throne, railway building had just begun but by 1870 there were 13 562 miles of track across the country. The Victorian age was an age of great inventors, scientists, writers and artists.

The postal service (known as the 'penny post') was invented in 1840 and telephone services began in 1890. The population grew so quickly that the Victorians struggled to cope with enormous health and housing problems. London had under 3 million inhabitants when the Victorian age began but was up to 6.5 million at the time of Victoria's death. The Victorians were great builders. They built more houses, more public buildings, more hospitals, schools and churches than anyone before them.

Find out more

● Choose two subjects from this list and write a few sentences about them.

royal palaces	royal events
Sandringham	Coronation
Balmoral	death of Prince Albert
Osbourne House	jubilee

CHAPTER 4

Name _____

Victorian people who made history (1)

When did these people live? What made them famous? Write a few sentences about them. The pictures will give you some clues but you will need to do further research.

William Gladstone

Emily Brontë

Florence Nightingale

Earl of Cardigan

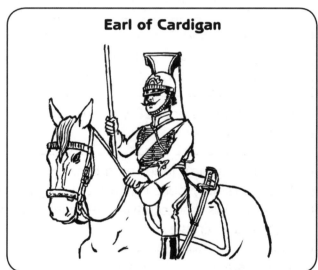

Joseph Turner

Charles Dickens

■SCHOLASTIC
www.scholastic.co.uk

Name _____

Victorian people who made history (2)

Find out when these people were born and when they died. What made them famous?
Use information books and other sources to write a paragraph about each one.

Isambard Kingdom Brunel

William Booth

David Livingstone

Charles Darwin

Dr Barnardo

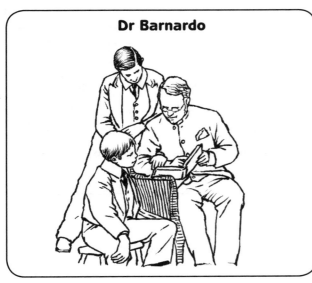

Annie Besant

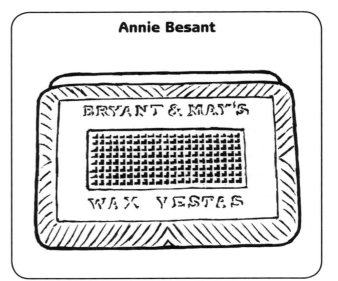

BRYANT & MAY'S

WAX VESTAS

Name _____

Poor children at work

● Study this picture of a Victorian child working as a trapper. Trappers were young children who opened doors for coal trucks down in the mines.

● Not everybody was poor in Victorian times, but for those who were, life was very tough – especially if you were a child. Poor children usually went to work in mines, mills and factories. Reasonable people were appalled when they learned how hard life was for children so the government sent inspectors to report on working conditions. People demanded that something be done about it. Read what the inspectors found out.

> **Boy aged 12**
> "I worked 12 hours a day down the pit and got 6d (2½ p) a day. I was so tired I fell asleep once and got thrashed."

> **A young child**
> "I don't like being in the pit. I work in the dark as a trapper."

> **Girl aged 13**
> "I work from 6 in the morning until 7 at night. I have an hour for dinner but my mother is very poor so I have no tea. My father was killed in the pit. Sometimes I have enough to eat, sometimes not."

> **Girl aged 12**
> "I know my letters but I can't spell my name. I earn a shilling (5p) a week which my mother keeps. I work from 6.30 in the morning until a quarter to nine at night."

● Compare a typical day in your life with that of a poor Victorian child.
● Imagine you lived in Victorian times. Design a poster or write a newspaper article to campaign against what was happening to Victorian children.

Timeline of change: Victorian schools

During Queen Victoria's reign the government decided that it must see that ordinary children had the chance to receive an education. These children would grow into adults who would be able to vote one day, so they must be educated! The children of the rich had always been educated privately.

● Some of the changes in schooling are listed below. Cut them out and put them on a timeline showing the order in which they happened.

Education in state schools was made free in 1891.

1846 – a teacher training scheme was begun.

In 1839 the government appointed Her Majesty's Inspectors to report on the quality of state-aided schools.

An Education Act was passed by Parliament in 1870 to allow Board Schools to be set up using public funds. They charged pupils a fee.

Education for children up to ten years old became compulsory by law in 1880.

In 1833 Parliament granted £20 000 to help the work of Church Schools that were educating the poor. This was the beginning of state education.

By the time of Queen Victoria's death in 1901, over 90 per cent of children aged five to 11 were enrolled in schools.

● Is there a Victorian school like this near where you live? Look for signs and clues. Does it have a bell tower? Separate entrances for boys and girls? Draw some sketches.

© M PLEDGE

Name _____

Decade decisions

Study these pictures. They belong to the three decades shown, but which one? Connect them to the correct decade.

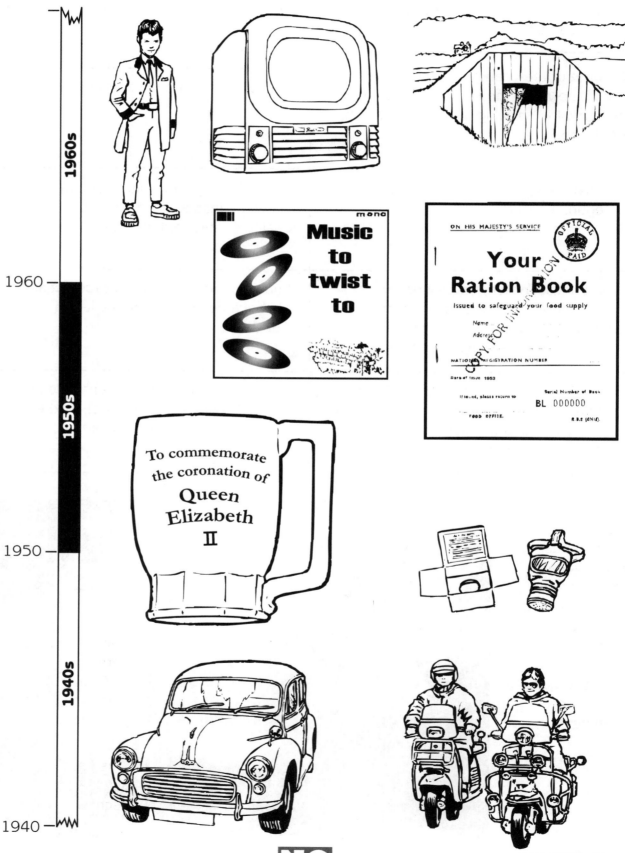

NO FUSS
PHOTOCOPIABLE

Changing faces: immigration

● Look carefully at this photograph. Write down four significant things that you notice about the people in it.

© TOPFOTO.CO.UK

1. _____

2. _____

3. _____

4. _____

On 22 June 1948, the ship *Empire Windrush* docked at Tilbury on the Thames estuary. It was carrying 492 passengers and 18 stowaways from Jamaica. As they all had British passports, they were entitled to come to Britain. The government gave many of them accommodation in a wartime deep shelter on Clapham Common that was used as an emergency hostel. The nearest Labour Exchange (a place to seek work) was Coldharbour Lane, Brixton.

● Imagine that you had just arrived on the *Windrush*. Write down your first impressions of Britain.
● Imagine that you were a British child living in Brixton at the time. Describe your first meeting with the newcomers.

Name _____

1950s' money

This is how money worked in the 1950s:

£1 was £1 just like today but it was made up of:

    240 pence (1 penny was written 1d)

    12d equalled one shilling (written 1/–)

    30d equalled a half-crown or 2 shillings and 6d (written 2/6)

IMAGES SUPPLIED BY THE ROYAL MINT © CROWN COPYRIGHT

● Confused? Try this shopping bill. Can you work out the total cost?

SID'S STORES
HIGH STREET, NEWTOWN

	£.s.d.
3 pints of milk at 6d a pint	
10lbs of potatoes at 1d per lb	
12 eggs at 4d each	
2lbs of flour at 6d per lb	

	pounds £	shillings s	pence d
milk			
potatoes			
eggs			
flour			
total			

● How many shillings made £1?

NO FUSS
PHOTOCOPIABLE

■ SCHOLASTIC
www.scholastic.co.uk

Wet and dry map

Use an atlas and any other useful reference book, to complete a wet and dry map of the world.

● Colour blue the parts of the world with very high rainfall.
● Colour red the parts of the world with very low rainfall.
● Label the main deserts of the world on your map.

NO FUSS
PHOTOCOPIABLE

Name _____

What use is water?

● Make a list of the uses of water and sort them under these headings.

Home	Farm	Industry	Leisure	Other
washing up	growing crops	cooling	water-skiing	firefighting

● Keep a record of the ways in which water is used in your home.

Monday	Tuesday	Wednesday	Thursday	Friday	Saturday	Sunday

■SCHOLASTIC
www.scholastic.co.uk

From reservoir to tap;
from dirty to clean

Water must be thoroughly cleaned before it is fit for us to use.

● First, water is collected in reservoirs where any solid material can settle to the bottom.

● Then water is pumped from the top of the reservoir into the treatment plant.

● In the treatment plant the water is flowed through filter beds of sand and gravel to remove any debris and smaller impurities. Chlorine is used to kill any germs that might be left in the water.

● The clean water is pumped into the water supply pipes and then travels to our homes.

Investigation

● Can you clean water? Take a small quantity of dirty pond water and clean it using the materials shown here. (Remember what you have just read.)

Remember!

When you have finished, do not drink your clean water. It may be cleaner than when you started but there will still be some invisible germs.

Name _____

Water costs money

● Study this water bill. Who supplies the water in this area? _____

● Who owns the water? _____

● What is the charge for water supply (before VAT)? _____

● Why is there a charge for used water? What does it mean? _____

_____

Severn Trent Water

Date (and tax point) 1 June 2000 Vat Reg No. 486 9555 65	Invoice No 959000035

Your account number

Account enquiries call (at local rate)

0845 6033 222

You can call us 8.00am to 5.00pm Monday to Friday

Dear Customer

This is your Water Services Invoice for the period 4 May to 30 May 2000.

The amount due is **£9.26**

The amount shown is payable within 7 days.

We are required to charge VAT on bills for customers whose Standard Industrial classification (SIC) Code falls within categories 1-5. The SIC Code held on our records is 48300 (Group 4). If this is incorrect please advise us in writing.

M = This is an actual reading

Water Services Invoice

Balance brought forward					£0.00
Sub Total					£0.00

Service	Meter No 97032	Latest reading	Previous reading	Volume (cubic metres)	Pence per cubic metre
Measured water supply		5(M)	0	5.00	77.08
Measured sewage				5.00	47.74
Measured Drainage - Comm Band 01					

Charges	VAT	Charge
Water Standing Charge	17.5	£1.17
Water Supply	17.5	£3.85
Used Water Standing Charge	Zero	£0.58
Used Water	Zero	£2.38
Surface Water Drainage Band 01	Zero	£0.40
Total charges for this period		£8.38

VAT @ 17.5%	£5.02	£0.88
VAT @ 0%	£3.36	£0.00
Total VAT		£0.88
Total charges including VAT		£9.26

Amount Due	**£9.26**

● Who supplies the water to your home? _____

● How much does your water cost? _____

● Do you have a water meter in your house? _____

● How does your bill compare with this one? _____

● Rain is free. Nobody owns it. Why should we pay for water? Write down some reasons.

SCHOLASTIC
www.scholastic.co.uk

Coastal zones

The zone where the land and sea meet is called the c _____ .
The sea can wear away cliffs and rocks.

Erosion landform

The sea can also build up the coast by deposits.

Depositional landform

● Study a map of a coastal area of Britain. (Use a geological map if you can.) Look
for **headlands** formed where the sea cannot wear away **hard rock**. Look for **bays and
beaches** where **soft rock** has been worn away by the sea.

● Using a map, make lists of places in Britain that are:

Headlands	Bays	Erosion landforms	Depositional landforms

Erosion

● Look at these photographs. Which erosion landforms do they show? Are they caves, arches or stacks?

> **Caves, arches** and **stacks** are examples of **erosion landforms** caused by the action of the sea.

1. _____

2. _____

3. _____

● Human activity can also cause coastal erosion. Can you think of any ways in which we do this?

● In June 1993, the Holbeck Hotel in Scarborough collapsed into the sea (see right). Find out how this happened. Write an illustrated report about it.

NO FUSS
PHOTOCOPIABLE

Name _____

The beach

The sea can carry sand and shingle and deposit it on the coast to form a beach. Beaches are the most common **depositional landform**.

● Look at the symbols on a large scale Ordnance Survey® map and find out what symbols are used to show:

sand beaches   shingle beaches

● What are the main differences between a sandy beach and a shingle beach? Describe them in your own words.

_____

_____

● Beaches sometimes have to be managed to keep them intact. Use a dictionary or encyclopedia to find out what the following are. Explain and illustrate the terms.

cliff-face armouring	groynes

artificial harbours	sea walls

CHAPTER 5

We do like to be beside the seaside

● Choose from the following the type of holiday you would most like to have.

● Use maps, books, the Internet and travel brochures to make a short **list** of suitable locations for the seaside holiday.

_____

_____

_____

_____

_____

● Choose one of these places and make a **brochure** about the place. Produce a holiday **itinerary**. Work out how you will travel and how long it will take to get there.

Structures (1): striking sounds

Investigate

> **You will need:** a tuning fork, a saucepan or similar lid, a bowl of water and a beater.

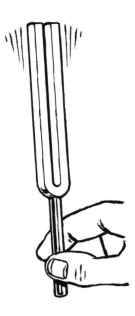

● Strike the tuning fork firmly (not too hard) on the edge of a wooden table. Stand it on the table. Listen to the sound it makes. How does it make this sound?

_____

● Strike the tuning fork again but this time dip it into a bowl of water. What happens? Can you explain why?

_____

● Hold the edge of the saucepan lid and strike it with the beater. Now suspend the lid and listen to the sound that it makes when you strike it. Is there a difference? Why?

_____

Invent

We have called this instrument a 'coat-clanger'.

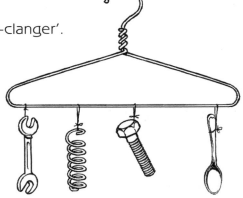

Here are some other 'clangers' we have invented.

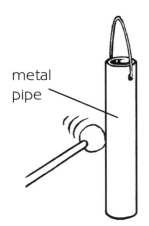

metal pipe

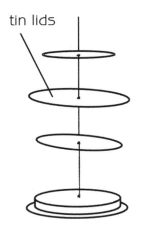

tin lids

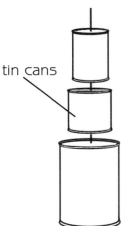

tin cans

● Design and make your own clanger instrument. Make sure that it is a quality instrument that will produce sounds that you can control. Give it a suitable name.

NO FUSS
PHOTOCOPIABLE

Name _____

Structures (2): tunes from tubes

Investigate

You will need: a piece of flexible hose (garden, shower or washing machine) at least 60cm long, card and sticky tape.

● Blow a raspberry with your lips pushed together (make a long juicy 'p' sound). Make your lips vibrate like a reed in an instrument.
● Put your lips against one end of the hose and blow your raspberry again.
● Tighten and loosen your lips to alter the sound. How many different sounds can you make?

Invent
We have called this one a 'raspberry blower's funnel-snake'.

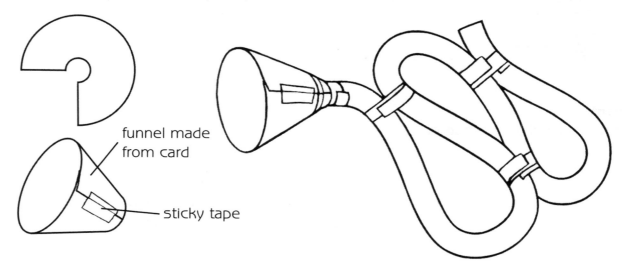

funnel made from card

sticky tape

Here are some other ideas for making a wind instrument using a tube.

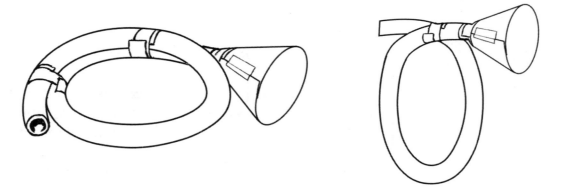

● Design and make your own instrument using a tube and a funnel. If you can, put a trumpet mouthpiece in the end. What difference does it make? Can you change the note the instrument produces? Give your instrument a suitable name.

www.scholastic.co.uk

Name _____

Using your loaf

● Add to this list of bread products.

soft white	wholemeal	soda	pitta
ciabatta			

● Keep a record of how much bread or bread products you eat in a week. Compare your results with a friend.

● Try out this basic bread recipe.

What to do

1. Mix flour, salt and yeast in a large bowl.

2. Make a well in the centre and add the oil and warm water.

Ingredients

400g strong white bread flour
3tbsp oil
7g active dried yeast
1tsp salt
250ml warm water

3. Mix to make a soft dough (add a little more water if too dry) – a round bladed knife may be used.

4. On a lightly floured surface, knead until the dough is smooth and elastic (about 10 minutes).

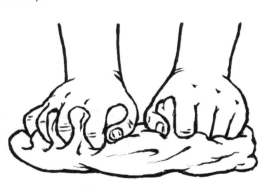

5. Place in a large lightly oiled bowl, cover with clingfilm and leave for about an hour until the dough has doubled in size.

6. Bake at 200°C for 35–40 minutes.

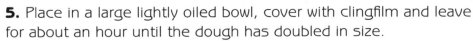

Name _____

Mechanisms (1): moving along

Investigate

● Draw a circle of radius 3cm on card. Cut it out. (You will find it useful to make more than one.)

● The challenge is to make your card circle move unaided in a straight line. Add any materials you wish that will enable the circle to roll down a slope in a straight line (without being pushed at the beginning).

> A **cam** changes rotary movement into movement in a straight line.

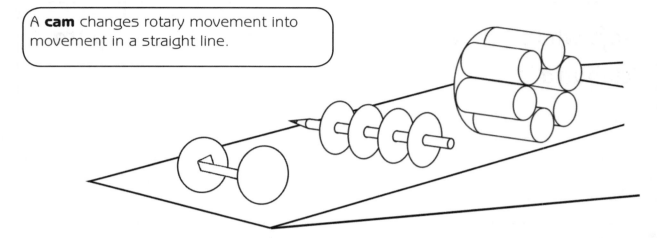

● What is the cam in your mechanism?

_____

● Here are some ideas to try.

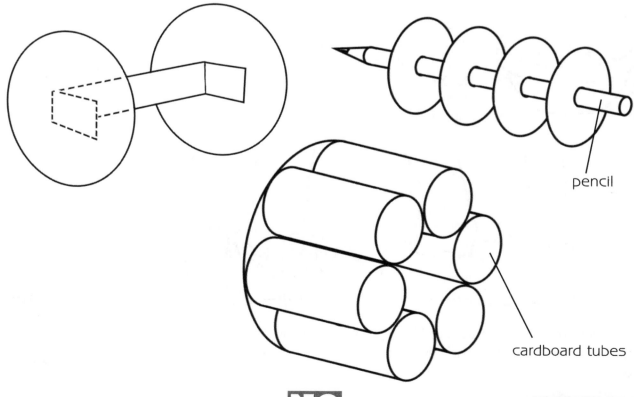

pencil

cardboard tubes

SCHOLASTIC
www.scholastic.co.uk

Mechanisms (2): moving around

Here are different ways of fixing wheels onto axles.

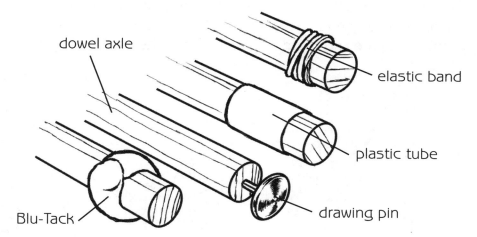

dowel axle

elastic band

plastic tube

Blu-Tack

drawing pin

The axle hole can be filed for a loose fit.

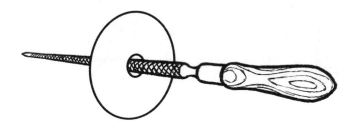

● Using any materials available, make a **Rollaround** using a cam mechanism that will enable a wheel to turn a corner as it rolls down a slope. You may need to use one of the methods above for your Rollaround machine.

Some ideas for Rollarounds

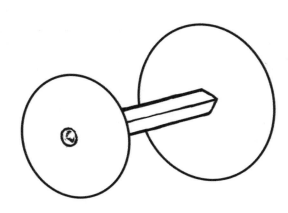

unequal wheels joined by an axle

a steering arrangement

● Describe how your mechanism works to a friend.

Name _____

Manipulating models

Imagine that the headteacher has put you in charge of planning a new play area in the corner of the school field. Use your computer to create a plan. Here is some of the apparatus you might wish to include. Make models of them on the screen using shapes and lines, moving them around to make the best arrangement.

First, draw a pencil sketch of your plan here.

Spreadsheet scoreboard

columns

	A	B	C	D	E	F	G	H	I	J
1										
2			[ ]							
3										
4										

rows

a cell

The scores of the five main batsmen in a cricket Test Match are quoted in the newspaper article below. Create a spreadsheet to show their scores in the three matches. Put the data into the correct cells. Use SUM **Σ** to find totals and insert a column to calculate the batsmen's average scores.

Test Match Review
In the first Test Ganguly scored 43 runs, Sehwag 71, Dravid 73, Singh 64 and Kaif 14. In the high scoring second Test Singh made 101 runs, Kaif only 8, Dravid a splendid 88, Sehwag 61 and Ganguly 10. But the third Test brought the best out of Ganguly who made 132 before he was caught on the boundary. Sehwag made 23, Dravid 66, but Singh was out for a duck although Kaif made 31.

Use your spreadsheet to find out:
● Which batsman had the best run average?

_____

● In which Test did the five batsmen's combined scores make the highest total?

_____

● If the scorer had made an error and recorded Ganguly's score as 10 in the second Test when it should have been 100, would it make any difference to your answers?

_____

Name _____

The cheapest school trip

Set up the spreadsheet below to handle the costings for a proposed residential school trip. There is a choice of five possible places to visit. There are 25 children going on the trip. The school's favourite coach company charges 11.5p per mile, per child, for the journey.

● Use formulae to calculate the data for the blank cells.

	A	B	C	D	E	F	G	H	I	J
1	Places	Miles	Travel cost (per child)	Travel cost (total)	Hotel cost (per child)	Hotel cost (total)	Excursions (per child)	Excursions (total)	Overall (per child)	Overall (total cost)
2	Broadstairs			£517.50		£2,550	£18			
3	Isle of Wight			£345.00		£2,125	£6			
4	Norfolk			£388.13		£1,875	£7.80			
5	Snowdonia			£235.75		£2,225	£8			
6	Whitby			£603.75		£1,975	£15.50			

● Now use the spreadsheet to find out:
– the cheapest trip

_____

– the most expensive trip.

_____

● Cut out all trips and museum visits. Does it change your last two answers?

_____

● The Shoestring Coach Company offers to transport the children for 6p per mile per child. What difference does this make to your answers?

_____

● Which trip would you choose? Explain your choice.

_____

● Which factor has the biggest influence on the cost of the trip?

_____

NO FUSS PHOTOCOPIABLE

■ SCHOLASTIC
www.scholastic.co.uk

Controlling devices

Some everyday devices rely on simple control features to make them work. Some devices require only one instruction.

● What makes this barrier operate? _____

_____

_____

Other devices require a sequence of instructions to operate.

● What happens here?

_____

_____

_____

_____

_____

● Think of other devices at home, in school, in the high street, that operate
on instructions. Fill in this chart with examples.

Device	single instruction	sequence of instructions

Name _____

Taking control

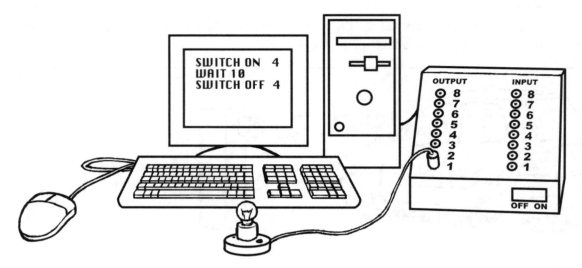

● Connect a light bulb to one end of a control box lead and put the jack plug into output socket 1.

The light can be switched off and on using control language and the control box software.

> SWITCH ON   1   (turns the light on)
>
> SWITCH OFF   1   (turns the light off)

● Put the jack plug into output socket 3. What commands would be needed to switch the light on and off now? Write them down.

_____

_____

_____

● Using the command WAIT, try a sequence of instructions before the enter key is pressed so that the light stays on for a certain number of seconds before being switched off. Write them down.

_____

_____

_____

● Connect a buzzer to another output socket. Write a procedure for the light bulb and the buzzer to operate in short bursts.

_____

_____

_____

Controlling traffic lights

● Here are some home-made traffic lights connected to a control box. Make a similar set and connect to a control box connected to a computer.

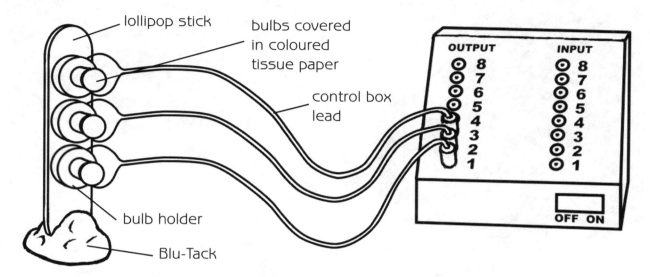

● Can you write a procedure using control language that will operate the lights in the correct sequence? We have started the procedure for you.

SWITCH ON 3 _____   _____

WAIT 3 _____   _____

SWITCH ON 2 _____   _____

WAIT 3 _____   _____

SWITCH OFF 3   2 _____   _____

● Try it out. Make changes if necessary.
● If you give the procedure a name such as FLASH, you can now REPEAT your procedure and the traffic lights will continue to operate. Try it!

REPEAT 10 _____

FLASH _____

END _____

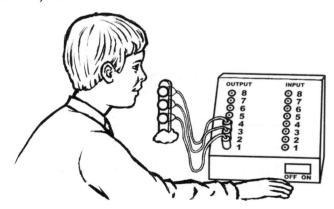

Name _____

Still life (1)

APPLES AND ORANGES, 1895-1900 (OIL ON CANVAS)
MUSEE D'ORSAY, PARIS, FRANCE, LAUROS/GIRAUDON/THE BRIDGEMAN ART LIBRARY

This painting is called _Apples and Oranges_ by Paul Cézanne. We call these sorts of pictures **still life**. Do you think that the name is a good one? Explain your answer.

_____

Subject: Describe what the artist has painted.

_____

Viewpoint: Describe the view the artist has taken. What difference would a closer viewpoint have made?

_____

Contrasts: What contrasts can you see?

_____

_____

3D: The artist has painted solid objects on flat paper. How has he made them look solid?

_____

Technique: What can you deduce from this picture about the techniques the artist used to paint it? How were different surfaces and textures created?

_____

Still life (2)

VAN GOGH'S BEDROOM AT ARLES, 1889 (OIL ON CANVAS)
ART INSTITUTE OF CHICAGO, IL, USA. / THE BRIDGEMAN ART LIBRARY

This is *The Bedroom* by Vincent Van Gogh. What do we call this sort of picture?

_____

Subject: Describe what the artist has painted.

_____

Viewpoint: Describe the view the artist has taken. What difference would a closer viewpoint have made?

_____

Contrasts: What contrasts can you see?

_____

_____

3D: The artist has painted solid objects on flat paper. How has he made them look solid?

_____

Technique: What can you deduce from this picture about the techniques the artist used to paint it? How were different surfaces and textures created?

_____

Name _____

Still life DIY

Here are some objects that you might find in your classroom.

● Choose a few objects like these (not too many) and arrange them together carefully for a still-life sketch. What surface will you place them on? Where is the light coming from? What background is there?
● Sketch them in your sketchbook.
● Change the arrangement of the objects, or your viewpoint and make more sketches.
● Choose your favourite sketch and make a painting from it.
– What kind of effect do you want to create?
– What colours will you use?
– Which paint?
– What size brushes?
– What kind of paper?

Urn, vessel, basket and pot

● Find one word that describes 'urn, vessel, basket and pot'.

(Use a thesaurus if necessary.) C _____

● Here are some examples made by some children.

They are called c _____ designs.

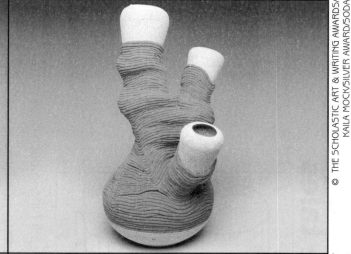

● Take each design in turn and answer these questions.
– What materials have been used for this container?
– What do you think it is for?
– Is it functional or decorative?
– Describe how you think it was made.

● Design and make a container. Decide its function first. Will it be purely decorative or have a particular purpose? Decide on the materials you will use. Make sketches and notes before you start.

Name _____

Textile tales

1.

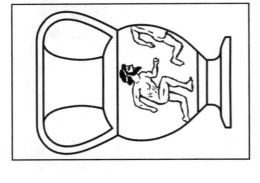

2.

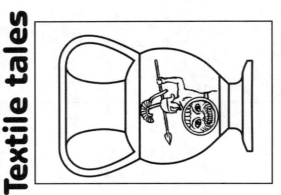

3.

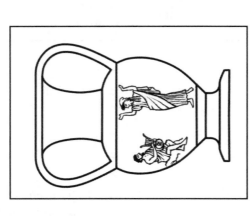

● The pictures on these Greek vases tell stories. Describe what is happening in each case.

● Textiles provide more room for telling a story. The story on this tapestry is a famous one. Describe what is happening. How do you think this was made?

NO FUSS
PHOTOCOPIABLE

■SCHOLASTIC
www.scholastic.co.uk

Tell a terrible tale in textiles

Read this story, then make a textile picture to illustrate it.

Odysseus and the Cyclops

On his long sea voyage, Odysseus met many terrible monsters, but none worse than the Cyclops. Giant, merciless creatures, they had a big single eye in the centre of their foreheads but spent most of their time as shepherds tending their sheep.

Odysseus landed his ship on the fertile land of the Cyclops and went with his men seeking the people who lived there. Unknowingly, they walked into the cave where lived the Cyclops Polyphemos, although he was out tending sheep at the time. When he returned, he exchanged a few words with Odysseus then picked up several of his men and ate them whole. The Cyclops then blocked the entrance to the cave with a stone that could not be moved.

Odysseus offered Polyphemos a bowl of strong wine to wash down the sailors he had eaten and when the Cyclops was completely drunk and asleep, Odysseus put a desperate plan into operation. With a red-hot stake heated in the fire, Odysseus and his men blinded the Cyclops in his single eye. Wild with pain, the Cyclops was unable to see to kill them.

Later, when Cyclops let the sheep out of the cave, Odysseus and his men escaped by hanging onto the underside of the sheep where the Cyclops could not feel them with his giant hands.

dyeing

knotting

quilting

stitching

printing

sewing

weaving

mounting

drawing

sticking

Name _____

Space odyssey

© Digital Vision Ltd

● What musical sounds might you use to describe a journey into space? What kind of sounds would fit the space-journey words below? Describe them.

Take off _____

Excitement _____

Fear _____

Weightlessness _____

Awe _____

Beauty _____

Darkness _____

Light _____

open

smooth

heavy

relaxed

light

urgent

loose

tight

textured

● Use any instruments to make these sounds. Try to create different moods. Add more sounds; take some away. Explore ways of improving the sounds you use to describe a 'Space Odyssey'.

NO FUSS
PHOTOCOPIABLE

■SCHOLASTIC
www.scholastic.co.uk

Name _____

Harmony or agony?

● Play these chime bars in turn from low C to higher C. Sing each note to 'lah'. Sing using the letter names for the notes. Sing and play!

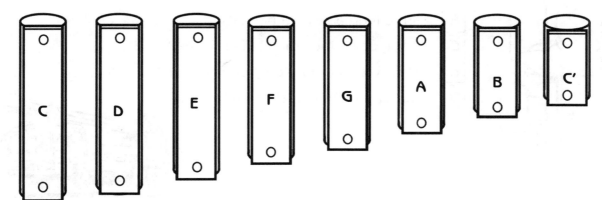

● This is called a scale. Sing up the scale C to C'. Sing down the scale C' to C.

● Choose any two chime bars from the scale above and play the notes together. How do they sound? Tense? Relaxed? Comfortable? Tight? Loose?

> If they fit easily together then this is called a **concord**. If they don't and the notes seem to argue with each other then this is called a **discord**.

● Try out different combinations of two notes from the scale and record your results.

_____

_____

_____

_____

_____

_____

_____

_____

_____

Name _____

Send round a fireman

A I am a fireman with a big hat,

B Sliding down the pole I land on a mat.

C Clang, clang! Ding, dong! goes my bell.

D Put out the fire and all is well.

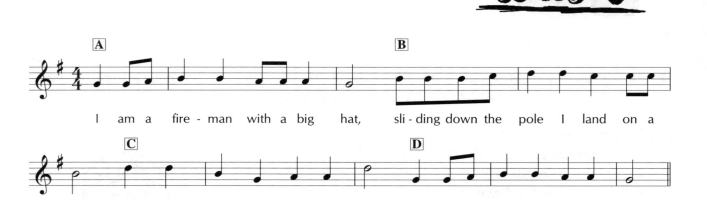

I am a fire - man with a big hat, sli - ding down the pole I land on a mat. Clang, clang! Ding, dong! goes my bell. Put out the fire and all is well.

● Learn to sing this song. You may be able to play it on your recorder.

● With your teacher's help, sing the song as a round. You can sing in two groups. The second group starts singing from the beginning when the first group reaches **C**.

Accompany the singing

● With a friend play all three of these notes at the same time on a slow, steady pulse while the class sing the round.

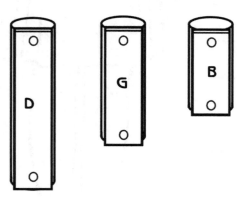

Playing the same chord over and over again like this is called a **drone**.

www.scholastic.co.uk

Name _____

Ostinato, drone and melody

● Here are various **drones** and **ostinati** written down in different ways. Play them and say which are ostinati and which are drones. You can play them to accompany 'Send round a fireman'.

1. 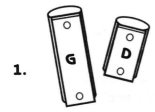   (play together)   _____

2. **B B**   **B**   **C**   **D**   (keep repeating)   _____
   Slid-ing   down   a   pole

3. **D**   **D**   **B**   **G**   (keep repeating)   _____
   Clang,   clang! Ding,   dong!

4. **B**   **B**   **G**   **G**   (repeat at a walk)   _____
   walk   walk   walk   walk

5. **G G**   **G G**   **D D**   **D D**   (repeat as   _____
   run-ning,   run-ning,   run-ning,   run-ning   a running rhythm)

6. 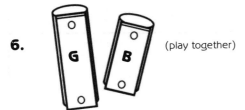   (play together)   _____

7.    (play together)   _____

● Play these arrangements with friends while the melody ('Send round a fireman') is being sung.

NO FUSS
PHOTOCOPIABLE

Name _____

Open and closed

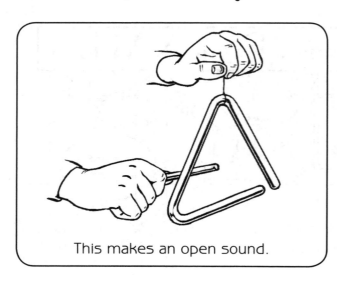

This makes an open sound.

This makes a closed sound.

Explore how to make open and closed sounds with these different instruments. Describe how you did it.

Instrument	Open	Closed
My choice		

NO FUSS PHOTOCOPIABLE

Keeping the pulse

On the beat...

Pulse keeper

● Play this pulse on a tambourine.

(walk   walk   walk   walk)

● Make these vehicles keep the pulse.

1.	2.
Big black motor car	High fly-ing jum-bo jet
3.	**4.**
Noi-sy, noi-sy, skateboards	Sleek white am-bu-lance

On the beat...

● Invent some vehicle phrases of your own. Make them 'keep the pulse'. Clap and say them while a friend plays the pulse (walk walk walk walk) on a tambour or drum.

Name _____

Islam: key words

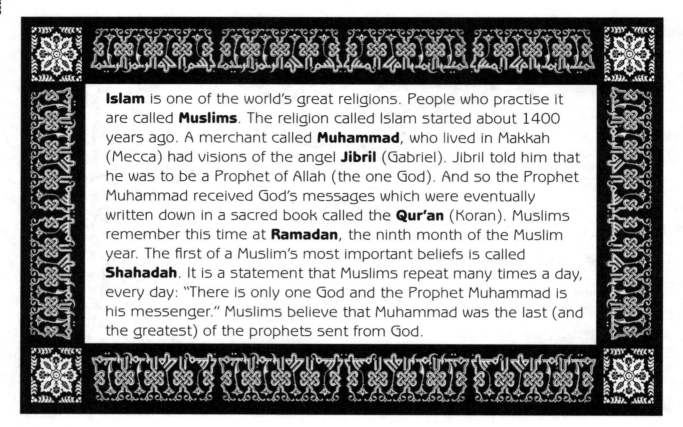

Islam is one of the world's great religions. People who practise it are called **Muslims**. The religion called Islam started about 1400 years ago. A merchant called **Muhammad**, who lived in Makkah (Mecca) had visions of the angel **Jibril** (Gabriel). Jibril told him that he was to be a Prophet of Allah (the one God). And so the Prophet Muhammad received God's messages which were eventually written down in a sacred book called the **Qur'an** (Koran). Muslims remember this time at **Ramadan**, the ninth month of the Muslim year. The first of a Muslim's most important beliefs is called **Shahadah**. It is a statement that Muslims repeat many times a day, every day: "There is only one God and the Prophet Muhammad is his messenger." Muslims believe that Muhammad was the last (and the greatest) of the prophets sent from God.

Fit the keys to the right padlocks.

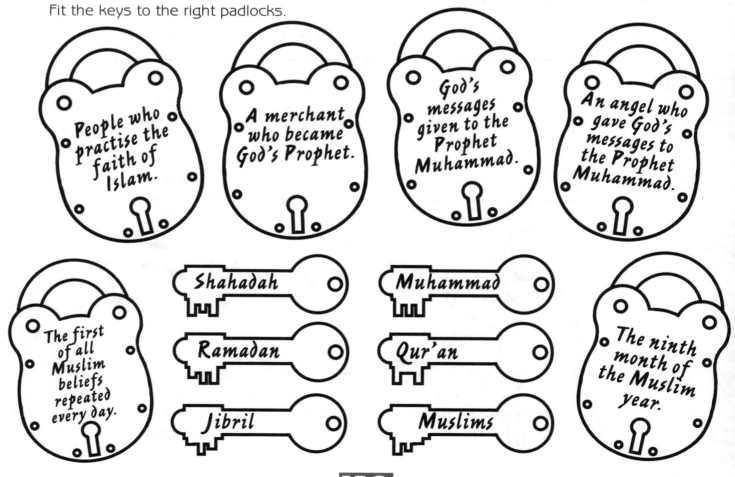

People who practise the faith of Islam.

A merchant who became God's Prophet.

God's messages given to the Prophet Muhammad.

An angel who gave God's messages to the Prophet Muhammad.

The first of all Muslim beliefs repeated every day.

Shahadah

Muhammad

Ramadan

Qur'an

Jibril

Muslims

The ninth month of the Muslim year.

NO FUSS
PHOTOCOPIABLE

■SCHOLASTIC
www.scholastic.co.uk

Five pillars

To be a Muslim you must carry out five important religious duties. These are thought of as **'pillars'** because, like pillars holding up a building, they hold up the Muslim faith.

Shahadah to repeat this important belief every day "There is only one God, Allah and the Prophet Muhammad is his messenger".

Salah to pray five times a day.

Zakah to give money to the poor.

Sawm to fast during Ramadan.

Hajj to go as a pilgrim to Makkah (Mecca), the holy city.

● Choose one pillar and find out more about it. Explain how Muslims carry out this duty.
● How do duties and rules help us? Talk about this with a friend.

Pilgrimage

● Look up **pilgrimages** in an encyclopedia. List places that people have visited on pilgrimages.

_____

_____

_____

_____

_____

A **pilgrimage** is a journey with a purpose. Pilgrims usually feel a need, inside themselves, that will only be satisfied by making a special journey. Some old soldiers make pilgrimages to battlefields where their friends were killed in battle. Religious people make journeys to holy places sometimes as a duty.

● A pilgrimage to the holy city **Makkah** (in Saudi Arabia) is one of the five pillars of Islam. It is a duty called the **Hajj**. Sort the following facts under these headings.

Where and when?	Who?	Why?	How?

On the Hajj, Muslims wear similar clothes (men – white, unsewn, cotton sheets and women – plain dresses).	Muslims dress alike on the Hajj to show that they are all the same in the sight of God.
Strict rules apply when they enter the holy city. These are called **ihram**.	Under ihram, pilgrims must not cut their hair or nails or kill any living thing.
Pilgrims also visit Madinah where the Prophet Muhammad is buried.	Every healthy Muslim who can afford it must go on the Hajj.
Muslim pilgrims travel from all over the world.	Under ihram, pilgrims must not wear perfume or jewellery.
The Hajj is a Muslim duty.	The Hajj takes place every year during the 12th month of the Muslim calendar.
The Hajj is a once in a lifetime journey.	

NO FUSS PHOTOCOPIABLE

SCHOLASTIC
www.scholastic.co.uk

A special book

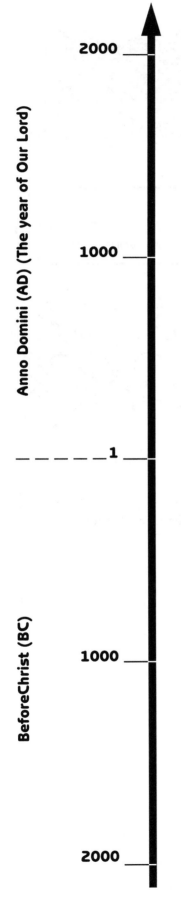

● Which do you think is the world's bestselling book?

_____

● Give two reasons why this might be.

_____

_____

Throughout the world dates are recorded in relation to the birth of Christ. BC is before Christ and AD (anno Domini – in the year of our Lord) is after Christ's birth. But it is difficult to be very accurate about dates a long time ago. We now believe that Christ was born in AD4.

● All these dates are connected to the Bible. Place them on the timeline. (We don't always bother to put AD with a date.)

| Abraham **1800BC** | Moses **1200BC** | King David **1000BC** |

| William Tyndale translated the Bible into English **1526** | Christ's crucifixion **AD30** |

First 'authorised' English Bible published **1611**

Greek copies of the New Testament were written on parchment (a codex) – oldest surviving from around **AD350**, the Codex Sinaiticus in the British Museum.

Name _____

Belief and action

Jesus gave these great commandments to his followers.

1.
Love the Lord your God with all your heart, and with all your soul, and with all your strength, and with all your mind.

PLEASE GIVE

2.
Love your neighbour as you love yourselves.

How might Christians put the second belief into action today? Think about events in the news. Think about your local area. List actions Christians could take.

Who needs help	What Christians could do

NO FUSS
PHOTOCOPIABLE

Love your neighbour

The first Christians were not always loved. The Romans often tried to kill them.

The Christians used a secret code to avoid being caught. They drew part of a fish in the dust – if the stranger completed it, they knew that the person was a Christian too. The Greek word for fish is ιΧθΥΣ.

The letters stood for
ι : Jesus
Χ : Christ
θ : God's
Υ : Son
Σ : Saviour

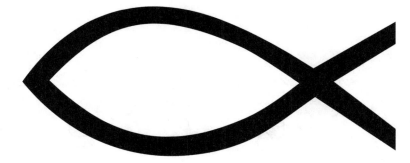

● Where do you see this sign today?

● But Christians were taught to love their neighbour. Who was their neighbour? Jesus taught his followers about neighbours using the story of the Good Samaritan. Read it for yourself (Luke 10: 29–38) and write captions for these pictures.

Name _____

Where am I? Who am I?

● Cut out these countries of Europe. Can you fit the puzzle together correctly? (You will need an atlas.) Mark where you live.
● Put a coloured border around all the countries that belong to the European Union (EU).
● Can you find out which countries want to join the EU?

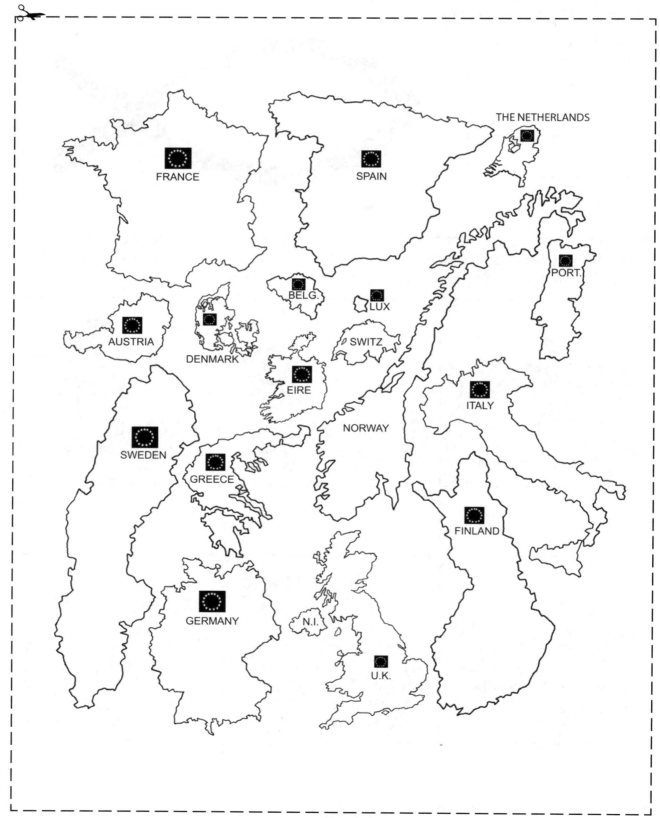

Name _____

My connections

I have connections with…

Place	Reason	Distance from home

People with power – your local authority

Your **local authority** gets money from a local tax called **council tax** and from the government. It has the **power** and right to do this because Britain is a **democracy**. This means that **councillors**, who run the local authority, must be **elected** by local people. The local authority has a **duty** to use this money to provide local **services**.

● The kind of local authority that you have depends on where you live. Find out about yours (a telephone directory may help).

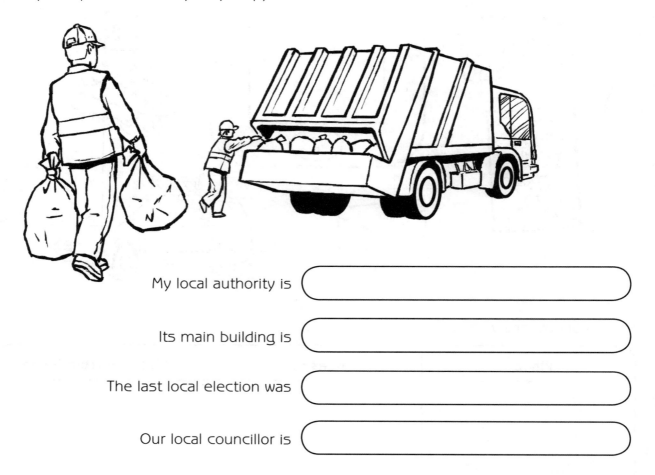

My local authority is (   )

Its main building is (   )

The last local election was (   )

Our local councillor is (   )

Services that my local authority provides	
Service	**Example**
Parks	
Education	

Feeling is understanding

Reading is not always easy but it is even harder when you cannot see. **Braille** was invented as a way of feeling words instead of seeing them. Letters are made from small raised dots on a 2-by-3 grid pattern. The dots can be felt with the fingertips.

● Find out what it is like to do this for yourself. Use sticky circles to raise the dots (in black) above the others on the paper. Cut out the letters to form your first name. If you need more letters, make them. Try reading without looking. Remember that your dots are much bigger than the real ones.

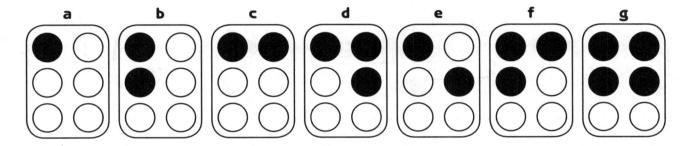

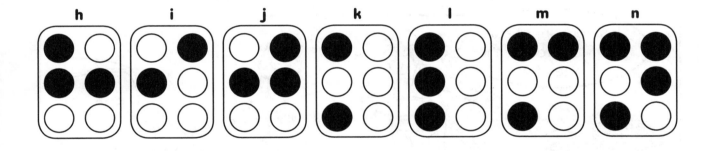

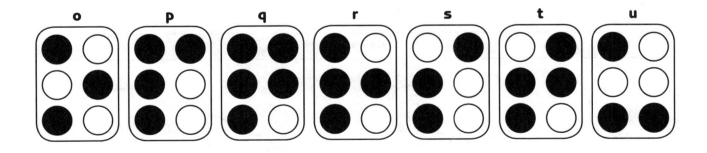

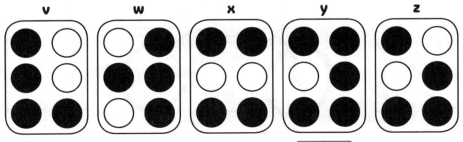

NO FUSS
PHOTOCOPIABLE

Name _____

What is important?

Trust

Honesty

Respect

Tolerant people might...

Tolerant people might...

_____

_____

_____

_____

_____

_____

Tolerant people might...

_____

_____

_____

_____

_____

_____

Tolerant people might...

_____

_____

_____

_____

_____

_____

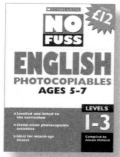 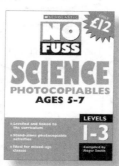   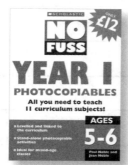 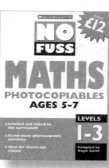  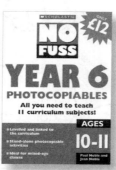 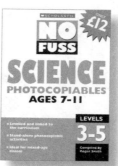 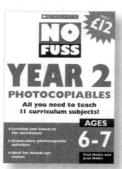  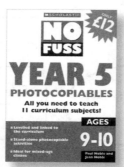

■SCHOLASTIC

In this series:

ISBN 978-1407-10093-7

ISBN 978-1407-10094-4

ISBN 978-1407-10095-1

ISBN 978-1407-10096-8

ISBN 978-1407-10097-5

ISBN 978-1407-10098-2

ISBN 978-0439-96548-4

ISBN 978-0439-96550-7

ISBN 978-0439-96552-1

ISBN 978-0439-96549-1

ISBN 978-0439-96551-4

ISBN 978-0439-96553-8

To find out more, call: 0845 603 9091
or visit our website www.scholastic.co.uk